YOUR
TIME
is
NOW

STEP INTO
YOUR GREATNESS

GREG S REID

Darrell,
Enlighten Yo.
Dave

step on
the dootka
and stont
your journey
Wayne

Darrell
Laugh often & take
risks often.

Hannah Watrous
1800 Nici Hat

Chase it Now!
#7 Coaster

Your Time is Now
Greg S. Reid

Sherpa Press
4616 W. Sahara Ave #308
Las Vegas, NV 89102

www.sherpapress.com

First published in the United States of America
by Sherpa Press in 2016

ISBN-13: 978-1-939078-07-0

Sherpa Press books may be purchased for
educational, business, or sales promotional use.

For information, please write:

Special Markets, Sherpa Press
4616 W. Sahara Ave #308
Las Vegas, NV 89102

YOUR TIME IS NOW

Chapter One	6
Chapter Two, featuring Eric Schneider	11
Chapter Three, featuring Wayne O'Day	23
Chapter Four, featuring Jeanne O'Neale	47
Chapter Five, featuring Dave Rowe	56
Chapter Six, featuring Hector Castillo	67
Chapter Seven, featuring Garth and Hannah Watrous	73
Chapter Eight. featuring Bryan Ells and Grant Moseley	81
Chapter Nine, featuring Joe Newkirk	87

Chapter Ten	97
Chapter Eleven, featuring Andrew Blume	103
Chapter Twelve, featuring Scott Carson	109
Chapter Thirteen, featuring Ma Gia Tri	115
Chapter Fourteen	120
Chapter Fifteen, featuring Liana Clulow	126
About Greg S. Reid	134
Our Contributors	136

"It's a terrible thing, I think, in life to wait until you're ready. I have this feeling now that actually no one is ever ready to do anything. There is almost no such thing as ready. There is only now. And you may as well do it now. Generally speaking, now is as good a time as any."

~ Hugh Laurie

CHAPTER ONE

If there ere was one thing Max knew, it was uncertainty. While some people turned everything they touched into gold, it seemed that everything in his life was in limbo. First, there was college. He was majoring in business, with a minor in marketing. However, neither seemed to fit; and the more classes he attended, the less interested he was. At that point in his life, he should have been getting closer to his goals, but every day pushed him further back.

His father owned a grocery store—not just any store, it was the largest natural food grocery store in a 60-mile radius of his hometown. His father had done everything right—he'd started from scratch and built his business from good old know how, long hours, and elbow grease. At one time, he'd done it all—mopping the floors, cleaning the coolers, stocking the shelves, manning the register, and charming the customers. His hard work had paid off, quite nicely, and now that his dad was in his upper 50s, it was "understood" that Max would get a degree and groom himself to one day take over the family business.

If it were only that simple.

Max knew the store—after all, he'd spent a great deal of his childhood there. After school, he sat in the office and did his homework at his father's desk. By the time he was ten, he was given a broom and told to get to work. The only paying job he'd ever had before college was stocking the shelves after school and on weekends. To some, it seemed like a successful future was ready made and waiting for him. Unfortunately, it wasn't the future Max wanted.

Max didn't like the grocery business. In high school, he dreaded having to go to work and couldn't imagine that store being his future every day for the rest of his life. When he was there, he was bored with the repetition, so much so that his dad had to prod him to keep working and finish the task at hand. Every day seemed like the last, and the only thing that changed were the people who walked through the doors. To compound matters, he found he hated business classes just as much. They, too, were boring, and it took everything he had to focus on his studies. To combat his boredom, his mind often wandered. Daydreaming had always been one of his downfalls.

He daydreamed about anything and everything—one day his mind would take him through an imaginary life as a major league pitcher, and before long, he'd find himself walking away from his books and grabbing his glove. Sports was his real love, and as far as he could tell, it didn't require a business degree. However, being a college student gave him the opportunity to play—and it kept his dream alive, that maybe, just maybe, he might get noticed and sent to the minors.

Max had never been a collegiate scholar. He was attending a state university on a baseball scholarship, which was probably the only reason he'd been accepted at the university. It certainly wasn't because of his "average" grades. The only classes he'd actually liked in high school were physical education, art, and computer-aided drafting and design. He could sit all day at the computer and design something out of nothing more than idea. When it worked, it was the most rewarding feeling he'd ever known—certainly better than inventorying vitamins, supplements, and organic fruits and vegetables.

Baseball was the reason he stayed in college. It was his incentive to crack the books and try to maintain a grade point average that would keep him on the team. Baseball was the only thing on his mind as he was running that March morning. The streets still held the residue of the light drizzle that had fallen in the early morning hours, but Max didn't mind as he pounded one foot in front of the other, determined to be in the best shape ever in his junior year—if there was a time when he might get noticed by an MLB scout, it was now.

With an even stride, he set his pace and got into rhythm, not even thinking about what he was doing. His mind was on the field—daydreaming about pitching his first collegiate no hitter. He looked into the stands and saw his dad, cheering loudly. Recruiters were lining up waiting to sign him to the minors, and his dad was beaming with pride, saying, "That's my son! He's gonna be a major league pitcher!"

As they say, the crowd went wild. Their roar

grew louder and louder ... cameras flashed, then dimmed. Suddenly, everything went black.

CHAPTER TWO

T he first thing he saw was a light—but it seemed so far away. He wanted to go to it, but he was being pulled back. He felt so light, but at the same time, so heavy. At first, he resisted the force that was holding him back, but try as he might, he couldn't move. As the light grew smaller and smaller, he protested, "Let me go! Let me go!"

A deep, but calm and comforting, voice interrupted him, "Go back. It's not your time."

The light disappeared, and as soon as it did, his body writhed with pain.

"Maxwell! Maxwell, can you hear me?"

He tried to talk, but the words didn't come out right. Opening his eyes, he found himself in a bright room—everything was white, so much so that it hurt his eyes. Blinking a few times helped his eyes adjust. Suddenly, a face came

11

into focus—a woman wearing a mask and cap.

"Do you know where you are, Maxwell?"

"Huh? Uh, no," he managed weakly.

"You're in the hospital. You just got out of surgery."

"What? … Why?"

"While running, you were hit by a car. You just had surgery to repair your leg and your arm. But overall, you're quite a lucky guy, Maxwell. Someone was watching over you today, young man."

"My arm … my arm. My right arm?"

"Yes. It's going to take some time to heal, but there shouldn't be any long-term damage. Your leg, though, is broken in three places. With physical therapy, you should be walking again, but it will take time. For now, you need to rest. When we move you into a room, you can see your parents."

* * * *

One Week Later

"Good morning, Max. My name is Kate, and I'm here to take you to rehab. Are you ready?"

His nurses had already moved him from his hospital bed to the wheelchair, where he'd been waiting since breakfast.

"Now's as good a time as any, I guess," he replied, though his tone didn't mirror his words. In fact, Max didn't care one way or another ... why bother? He couldn't walk, and his baseball career was over.

Kate wheeled him down the hall and into the elevator. The ride to the fifth floor took no time at all. When the doors opened, they found themselves in a huge room with every type of exercise equipment imaginable. To the side was a small waiting area, with a sofa, chairs, and tables covered with magazines,

"I'm going to leave you here, Max. Your therapist will be with you in just a few minutes."

Not knowing what to expect, Max was uncomfortable. He thought about grabbing a magazine to kill time, but that didn't appeal to him, either. He wondered just what kind of rehab he could possibly do—for all intents and purposes, his leg was out of commission and the cast on his arm prevented any movement there, too. Dismissing the magazines, he lifted his head and caught the eye of a man with dark hair sitting in a chair across from him.

"Good morning," he said.

Max nodded in reply. Conversation just wasn't his thing lately. He was too busy feeling sorry for himself.

"My name is Eric Schneider, and you are?"

"Max. Maxwell Clark."

"Nice to meet you, man. If you don't mind my saying it, it looks like you've seen better times."

"Yeah, I was hit by a car—the car ran a stop sign and wrecked my life. So yeah, I've seen better times."

The man didn't flinch a bit and continued just as cheerily as before, "So, Max, tell me what you do."

"I'm in college and was a starting pitcher for the university's baseball team. But not anymore. I can't go to school. I can't pitch. I can't do anything. I guess I don't know what I do or what I'm going to do."

"I've never been hit by a car, but I have been in your position—not knowing what to do, I mean. I guess you could say I had to reinvent myself."

"What do you mean? What do you do?" Max asked, suddenly finding himself interested in what this man had to say.

"Max, I turn trash into gold. Actually, I have a recycling business. We started with paper, but we've expanded far beyond in the last three generations. At one time, though, this wasn't what I wanted to do. It was my dad's business when I was younger like you, fresh out of college. But I didn't want to work in the trash industry—I wanted to be in the music business. That dream did not pan out for me, so I approached my father and asked if I could come to work for him. I did so for 4-1/2 years, yet something felt missing, something inside said, "This is not right; there must be something else out there."

"What I didn't know was everything I was looking for was right in front of me. It took me years to realize that, but like most 27 year olds, I didn't know that at the time. I disconnected myself completely, and that's how I began to reinvent who I am."

"What did you do?"

"You won't believe this, but I packed up and moved to Maui."

"Wow. That sounds like fun."

"It was fun, *and* it was different. I lived there for eight years, Max. My wife and I lived off the grid, had two kids, and even experienced community living there."

"When I left for Maui, I knew I wanted something more, something that fulfilled my heart—kind of like the way you feel about baseball. Everybody looked at me and joked about that, but I wondered what was so funny about it … why is finding what fulfills you something that people talk about but don't ever do?"

"I know—that's exactly how I feel. You see, my dad wants me to follow in his footsteps, too—he owns Clark's Natural Foods. Maybe you've heard of them?"

"I have, Max. That's quite a business he's got there."

"I know, and my dad loves it. But I guess I'm like you when you were younger—it's just not what I want to do. Trouble is, I don't know what I want to do, especially now," he said, looking down at his leg.

"Well, neither did I. I didn't have the answers then, so I left the comfort zone of what I knew in search of something different, something exciting, and, yes, risky. Maui was that place for me. There, I experienced life in an entirely different realm from my urban surroundings of Chicago. We lived in a community, on a bio dynamic farm, and on an avocado farm. We built a small schoolhouse, I worked various jobs, and I became part of a men's group. In those experiences, I began to look within, I began to share truths with my friends and family (sometimes that went well, and other times it did not), and I began to see myself with new eyes.

"I guess you could say I learned who I was, Max. I had to find me and who I really was and step into it. And I had to do it free of opinions and labels. Maui gave me that opportunity."

"Hmmm, that sounds like the way I feel," Max offered.

"Well, my story takes an interesting turn, and I think, given time, yours will, too. My last job in Maui was in real estate. I won't lie—it was exciting. It was the first time I'd found a job and a career that would support me and my family on a new level. Then, in 2007, when I had five deals in escrow, the real estate market fell apart. Within a week, all five of those deals fell through, too. I had no savings and no income. Needless to say, I was extremely frustrated, scared, and down—probably much like you're feeling now."

"Wow. So what did you do?"

"I sat at home, scared and feeling like a failure. A few days later, Max, my wife was on the phone with my mom, who told her that my dad needed knee replacement surgery, but he didn't feel comfortable or confident enough to leave the business for a month. It was my wife who came up with the idea for me to call my dad and ask for help; the truth was we both needed help. When I did, it felt good. It felt right. There I was talking to my dad and sharing my fears and failures. But the burden lifted and instead of feeling doomed, I actually started to feel excited."

"Two weeks later, Max, I was back home, staying in my parents' home. When I walked into 'the office' that first time back, I noticed my desk was still there. I realized everything I had written off seemed different. I saw love, I saw possibility, and I saw legacy. You could say a veil had been lifted and I saw my own potential."

"I said, 'This is my time.' Since then, Max, I became everything I always knew I could be, and I continue to redefine what that looks like. I had to start from ground zero, but it's been awesome, and my relationship with my father has never been better."

"That's a neat story, Eric. Like you, my dad wants me to take over the family business. But that's not what I want to do."

"That's okay. You see, sometimes we need to take time off ... a step back to learn who we are and what we really want. I believe I was given my experience as an opportunity to do that. The first step was acknowledging where I was; that was huge. Max, you cannot move forward until you acknowledge where you are right now—that's something you might have needed to do even before your accident."

"I guess you're right. I was living for one thing—baseball. But everything in my life hinged on it. I had no real plans for the future. In fact," he laughed, "I even kidded myself into thinking I was going to make the majors."

"That might have happened. Who knows? But one thing will always be true, Max—things change. When they do, whatever the situation, the story, or the circumstances, those things are just things. What I've found that works is to learn what is underneath the story—what are your feelings or beliefs about yourself? What is the story you make up about yourself now, Max? Recognize that there are many parts of who you are, and all the parts make up the whole—the good, the bad, and the ugly. Baseball was only a part of who you are, too. Your accident is like my Maui—it's a blessing in disguise—an opportunity for you to reinvent yourself and discover who you really are and what you really want to do."

"I never looked at it that way before. But I don't even know where to begin."

"My advice to you is to ask yourself, 'What's possible now?' It's okay to feel scared or down—we all do from time to time. But you can choose your attitude. You might go into the family business, and you might do something entirely different. I won't say it's going to be easy, but I will say that when it's easy, it's boring. Anything is possible, and I want you to remember that. Now is your time to formulate your ideas so you can take the steps to make them happen."

"I just wish I had a clue where to begin."

"It might help to start out with a mission. Max, when I returned to Chicago, there were many cool things that unfolded. One of those was finding the Mankind Project, just six blocks from the business. You see, that men's group I was part of in Maui was started by a group of my friends and was based on the teachings of the Mankind Project, specifically The New Warrior Training Adventure. One of the key things I walked out of that training with was a mission. My mission is to create a world of cosmic, comedic, and soulful relationships by listening for love. It was from that place that I was able to take all my past experiences and put them into action in my current situation. It was from that place I was, and still am, focused on now, and why I do what I do in this world, for my company, for my family, my friends, and the world at large."

Max let that soak in for a minute. Here was a man who had lost not only his job, but his career … and because of it, he was able to help the family business prosper and become even more successful. In the end, his goal was to help others. *Now, here he is, a complete stranger, offering me advice.*

"Remember, even when it feels like everything is lost, it's just an opportunity to reinvent yourself. What I was looking for was there the whole time—I just couldn't see it. What you're looking for is there, too. This is your time, Max, to find it."

Eric looked up and smiled. "It looks like my dad's done with therapy. It's been great talking to you, Max. Maybe we'll see you here again."

"I'd like that. It's been great talking to you," Max said. "But I'm hoping to go home soon, so I'm not sure when or where I'll have physical therapy."

"In that case, here's my card. Keep in touch and let me know how you're doing, please. You're a bright guy with a bright future ahead of you, and if there's any way I can help you, I will."

"I'll be sure to do that. And, Eric ... thank you so much. I really enjoyed talking with you."

CHAPTER THREE

Like Eric had said, it wasn't going to be easy. Rehab surely wasn't. Max thought he was in good condition, but he found the simplest exercises to be exhausting. His physical therapist, though, wouldn't let up for a second.

"C'mon, man, you can do it!" Keith prodded him to keep going. He'd explained that their focus was to strengthen the muscles that would have to work harder so he could mobilize his wheelchair—something that wasn't easy to do with one arm in a cast. Max had always prided himself on being in good shape, but Keith proved him wrong.

"You're like a drill sergeant," Max said. It had taken every bit of strength and energy he had to complete one set of exercises.

"You haven't seen anything yet," Keith laughed.

It was Keith's humor that kept Max going. In fact, if it wasn't for Keith, he would have given up on day one. But Keith had a great attitude—he was young and funny ... and he talked to Max like one of the guys. Max wouldn't admit it, but even though rehab was grueling, he looked forward to it. And it was all because of Keith.

"Hey, man, how many pitches can you throw in a game?"

"I can usually throw 100 without a problem—though I've thrown more."

"That's impressive. Well, if you can throw 100 pitches, I think you can do 10 more reps."

"That's easy for you to say, Keith, but maybe I should do as you do, not as you say," Max said, laughing. Keith brought new meaning to "push through the pain," but Max truly enjoyed working with him.

"Oh, no—this isn't about me. It's all about you. When I'm done with you, you're going to be ready to take on anything."

"Good, cuz I need to do something—sitting around this hospital is getting boring. I think I'll scream if I have to sit through another night of sitcom reruns. I couldn't imagine being here all of the time—don't you do anything for fun around here?"

"Yeah, we harass our patients," Keith shot back. "No, seriously, I know nobody *wants* to be here—they *have* to be here. And it's like their lives are on hold while they're here … they're waiting—waiting to get well, waiting to go home, waiting to go back to work. We know that, which is why we do try to make it easier for them during their stay when we can."

"How so?"

"Well, we have movie nights every month. And then there's the library. Has anyone taken you there yet?"

"No. I haven't heard about it," Max replied.

"Well, let's fix that when we're done. I have a break coming up. If you'd like, I'll show you where it is."

Exactly 12 minutes later, Keith proclaimed that their session was over and took him down to the second floor to see the library. Max wasn't sure what he expected, but he was surprised to see that there were hundreds of books lining the walls.

"Pretty impressive," he said, not realizing he was thinking out loud.

"Yes. As you can see, most of the books in our library are inspirational and motivational, and for good reason. When people are sick or injured, it's easy to become depressed or want to give up. These books were carefully chosen for their positive messages of encouragement. I even come here and check out a book from time to time. You know, the one thing I've learned from these books and many others is that we all have a purpose in life, Max. And we're sent here to fulfill that purpose. It's called our passion—I know that to be true. I'm passionate about what I do and love helping people and watching them make progress. You have a purpose, too, Max. It might not be what you thought it would be, but now is the time for you to discover what it is and set your mind to it. Think of it as mental conditioning, rather than physical conditioning."

Max thought about Keith's words. He thought about telling him about the dream he'd had after the accident, the one where he was told it wasn't his time. But he decided not to—not yet. Still, maybe there was something to what Keith was saying—we have a purpose to fulfill while we're here, and Max hadn't yet found what it was.

"What would you recommend I read, Keith? I've never been a big reader, but I'd like to check them out."

"Well, I've always been fond of Napoleon Hill's *Think and Grow Rich*. Oh, and you might enjoy *Three Feet from Gold* or any of the books in that section."

In the end, Max borrowed three, thinking it was more books than he'd voluntarily read in his whole life.

"When you're done with those, let me know—we'll get more. You know, I was thinking ... sometimes it's really powerful when you hear these motivators in person. A guy by the name of Wayne O'Day is giving a presentation in the auditorium tonight. He was once a patient here, too. I hear he's got quite a story—do you want to go?"

"Really! Do I! Can I?" The opportunity to do something, anything, but stay in his hospital room excited him more than he realized.

"Yes, you can. I tell you what, I'll make the arrangements with your nurses, and I'll personally pick you up and wheel you down. Be ready at 6:00."

* * * *

Keith was true to his word and arrived a couple minutes before six.

"I'm ready," Max said, eagerly pushing away his dinner tray.

"Ah, good old Jell-O—a hospital staple. How is it?"

"Same as it was yesterday and the day before that," Max laughed.

"And there's more where that came from," Keith laughed. "C'mon, I want to get there before the good seats are taken."

The auditorium was nearly full when they arrived, but Keith managed to find a seat near the aisle where there was room to accommodate Max's wheelchair. Taking in his surroundings, it was hard for Max to believe they were still in the hospital. The auditorium was tastefully decorated. The dark mahogany floors perfectly complemented the plush theater-style seats and the artwork—which Keith pointed out were all original landscapes painted by local artists. Actually, Max thought it looked more like a fine hotel than a hospital.

As the overhead lights dimmed, the stage lit up, and a woman introduced the speaker for the evening: Wayne O'Day. After thanking the audience for his reception, he launched right into his speech. Max found himself listening intently to his story. Before long, he forgot his plight and was totally caught up in the plight of the speaker.

"In September, 2009, my life changed. As a retired airline executive, I felt my engines stop turning at 35,000 feet and I was free falling out of the sky.

What started as a routine morning ended with US Marshalls, sirens blaring, pulling me over and serving me a subpoena to appear before a Federal Grand Jury for my involvement as the CFO of Sands of Gold, a 20,000 acre, master-planned second-home development south of Acapulco, Mexico.

This couldn't have come at a worse time. I was recovering from two different heart procedures, and I had several investment properties in southwest Florida that were being foreclosed on.

As a finance guy, I was used to dotting my "I's" and crossing my "T's," but nothing in my 30-year career on United Airlines' finance team prepared me for what I was about to go through.

I had been hired ten months earlier by two partners, Frank and Jim, who needed a CFO to help obtain funding for their Mexican Second Home project. The project was located 90 minutes south of Acapulco, Mexico on the Pacific coast in a small town called Playa Ventura.

At the time, I was working on a project in Little Exuma, Bahamas, trying to find a joint venture partner for a developer. I arranged a conference with the Oppenheimer Family Trust. It was an uphill battle between two strong-willed parties. I was having difficulty finding middle ground.

I had recently returned from SIMA, The Spanish "Holiday Home Expo" in Madrid. While there, I entered a marketing relationship with Grupo Mall, a Spanish development company that was developing Campeche Playa, a master planned resort community on the beach in Campeche, Mexico. I planned to market the amenity-rich, attractively-priced project to Americans who were priced out of the Florida and Las Vegas markets.

Stewart Title writes title insurance in Mexico, and Mainstreet Board of Realtors, the sixth largest in the country, was offering a seminar on how Americans could buy beachfront property with title insurance in Mexico. Secure title would be important to any future client. I attended the seminar and sat across from Frank's brother, Richard. During the seminar, Richard told me about Sands of Gold and advised they were looking for realtors in the US to promote and sell their project and invited me to join other realtors who were already marketing the property.

Prior to entering a marketing agreement, I traveled to Mexico to see the project. I walked the beaches and reviewed the master plan, which was created by a world-class planner. In the narrative, the planner gushed about the natural beauty. In real life, the project was AWESOME: 20,000 acres overlooking the Pacific Ocean with a crescent beach every bit as nice as Marco Island, Florida. All was in order. I signed a marketing agreement and began promoting Sands of Gold. We had plans to promote Campeche at Miami's International Real Estate Convention, and we added Sands of Gold to our offerings.

Upon returning from Miami, I had a meeting with Frank and Jim to discuss our marketing strategy. At the end of the meeting, Frank asked if I would come on board as the CFO for Sands of Gold. He stated they needed a finance guy to procure a loan so building could be started and was willing to offer an equity position in the project. I was interested.

I deliberated for a few days and discussed it with my wife, Lili. I negotiated my contract and was part of the team. Hitting the ground running, I busied myself meeting with the finance team and developing the financial projections necessary to procure project funding.

As time went on, I became aware of Frank and Jim's related business. They had solicited millions from private individuals to flip foreclosed homes in Illinois. While I knew of the business, it was off my radar as my association was solely with the Mexican corporation, Sands of Gold. Ultimately, the US government identified their flipping business as a possible Ponzi scheme, which was the basis for the subpoena.

While I was looking for $500 million to develop Sands of Gold, the US economy was melting down. Lehman Brothers had declared bankruptcy in September, 2008 and created a whirlpool that would ultimately vicariate US homeowners' equity at a pace and level not seen since the 1930's. The whirlpool spilled over globally and took with it the Sands of Gold project. Jim and Frank's investors began to call, asking about their investments. They were all anxious and looking to me for reassurance. I directed them back to Jim and Frank and focused my discussion on the incredible potential of Sands of Gold.

In the end, the Mexican second home market had tanked, and the worldwide financial crisis would preclude selling any homes at a price needed to sustain the project. I resigned and walked away in early 2009.

Simultaneously, my wife and I were investors in expensive real estate in Naples, Florida, including a penthouse overlooking the Gulf of Mexico and a golf course single-family home, complete with pool and hot tub; both had appraised for $1 million at the time of purchase in 2006. The financial crisis caused their value to plummet. We could not sell, and business had deteriorated to a level that precluded keeping them. Ultimately, both were lost to the real estate pandemic that swept the country. The penthouse sold for $200,000, the golf course home slightly more.

Lili and I were in a very desperate position. Our investments in Naples had collapsed; nothing could be sold at a profit. We had exhausted our reserves, servicing debt on our rapidly depreciating real estate portfolio. Our other Illinois real estate investments had lost value and were struggling to perform. We had gone all in and were approaching a cataclysmic bust when the US Marshalls pulled me over.

By the time the US Marshalls subpoenaed me, I had already hired a pricy Chicago lawyers to defend myself from the Illinois Secretary of State for possible SEC Violations related to Frank and Jim's REO flipping business.

It was a very dark time in our lives—darker than any we'd ever experienced in our 30 years of life together. This biblical plague of darkness was consuming every aspect of our lives. I had two choices: 1) do nothing and be consumed by the darkness, or 2) find a way out. I kept telling myself over and over "Every Journey Begins in Darkness."

The most difficult part of any journey is the first step. I started walking slowly and eventually found my way to the Federal Defender Program in Rockford, Illinois, and was assigned a crusty, pipe smoking defense attorney named Paul Gaziano and his colleague, Kris Carpenter, a delightful lady several decades younger than Paul.

Lili and I drove two hours each way to our first meeting. We arrived early and were buzzed into the secured and reinforced office of the Federal Defender in Rockford. A little while later, Paul, wearing suspenders and smelling of pipe smoke, came into the waiting room. He quickly separated me from Lili and ushered me into a conference room that looked like it came right out of the 50's vintage detective show, *Dragnet*.

He introduced himself as Paul Gaziano. He advised me he had 30 years' experience in criminal defense. He also made the point that a Grand Jury had the authority and the power to indict a ham sandwich should it so choose. He had my attention.

He asked me to tell him about Sands of Gold, Frank and Jim, and my involvement. For the next two hours, I did most of the talking. When I left, I had the feeling that Paul took everything I said with a boulder-sized grain of salt. On the drive home, I told Lili about the meeting and felt very sorry for myself. How could I be facing jail time when I did nothing wrong? I had been very careful to separate myself and Sands of Gold from Frank and Jim's investors. I had focused on funding Sands of Gold to bring it out of the ground and the immense profits the project could produce. I thought to myself, "Bad things do happen to good people."

When I woke up the next morning, I started putting the pieces together. Frank and Jim had used me. In Frank's regular communications to their investors, he promoted me, my financial background, and my experience in real estate investing. In retrospect, he was using me to buy time. Their investors were restless and worried by the financial crisis, and they wanted their money back. Frank and Jim were unable to return the money or deliver the exorbitant returns they had promised. They needed more time to find an exit plan.

In the mind's eye of the investors, I was part of the problems. As they realized legal action would be required to recover their investment, the crosshairs were fixed on me. I was in a bad place, out of money, subpoenaed by the grand jury, and possibly facing prison time.

Other men would have been broken. I did what I have always done—woke up the next morning, got up, and brushed myself off. In my mind, I was first a survivor and second a winner. My mantra is WINNERS ALWAYS GET UP.

I put together a very large binder detailing my involvement with Sands of Gold and Fed Ex'd a copy to Paul. I thought I had proven beyond a doubt that I was innocent. When I met with Paul a few weeks later, he had other thoughts.

Paul grilled me about items I included in the binder. For the hour and a half we spent together, I defended myself over and over again. Paul ended the session by stating there was still a chance that I could go to jail. He went on to say that he was going to ask Assistant US Attorney Scott Verseman to grant me a proffer, instead of making me testify before the Grand Jury.

Paul explained that a proffer session, sometimes called "Queen for the Day," is a meeting between the suspect (me) and the US Attorney and other law enforcement agencies, where they are allowed to ask me questions. Any insight they garnered during the meeting would not be held against me in court. Those were the rules. My philosophy has always been to surround myself with the best professionals I could afford, so I agreed to Paul's proffer strategy, but went home very concerned.

Paul called a week later and advised me that Scott had agreed to the proffer. The day of the proffer, Paul advised me that only I would be allowed to talk. He would be next to me as my witness, but would not speak.

We left Paul's office and walked to the courthouse for the proffer. The walk seemed to take hours, but was really less than five minutes. We walked into a conference room where five men were seated around a large table. One of them stood. It was the Devil. He was younger, taller, and thinner than me with neatly styled blonde hair and piercing blue eyes. I felt him looking into my soul. Out of habit, I extended my hand to the man that could be sending me to prison. He introduced himself as Scott Verseman, the Assistant US Attorney who was leading the Grand Jury. He introduced the others, who were investigators from the FBI, IRS, and Postal Service.

Scott led the parade and started asking me questions, though I suspected he already knew the answers. After about 15 minutes, things got tense. The questions were tougher and came from the position, "As CFO, you should have known." After about an hour, Paul asked for a five-minute recess so we could talk.

When we stepped into the hall, Paul advised me that I was holding my own. That was about as good as it got with Paul. He made a few other suggestions about items he wanted me to disclose. I took a few deep breaths and walked back into the inquisition.

Not knowing if I was winning or losing, I defended myself. I just kept fouling off Scott's pitches as they came across the outside corners of the plate. I wanted to avoid the Grand Jury. At the same time, I was praying for one down the middle, one that I could hit out of the park.

At the end of the second hour, Scott slid a piece of paper across the table. It was an email Frank sent to his investors after I had resigned. Frank's message was that I left because I was adverse to risk. He went on to say that "we" (Frank, Jim, and the investors) had not come this far by being adverse to risk. Scott asked me the open-ended question, "What did this mean?" THERE IT WAS! It was my question, right down the middle, just like I hoped. I swung hard!

My answer was short and succinct. "If you take investors' money, you have a fiduciary responsibility to do with that money what you promised your investors or your lender. It is not yours to do with as you please." This had been a very contentious issue between me and Chairman Frank. This polarization was one of the validations I used to conclude I was being used and needed to resign. Seeing the email confirmed, in my mind, that I had made the right decision.

Scott put the email back in his file. He asked a few more questions, and the proffer was done.

We walked out of the room. I did not feel like a king or a queen; I felt numb. Paul advised me that I had done well. From him, that was a big compliment. He went on to say that I had not surprised him in the proffer and then advised me that he would follow up with Scott Verseman in about a week and would give me a call.

I thought about Paul's comment on the way

home. What was the meaning? Was he frequently surprised by what his clients disclosed under pressure? Then doubt started to set in. I thought about what I should have said. I questioned whether my arguments were compelling enough to avoid the Grand Jury. I relived the proffer over and over in my mind. When I pulled into the driveway, I had no recollection of the 90-minute drive from Rockford. I went into the house and collapsed on the couch, wondering if Scott Verseman believed I was a criminal.

A week later, Paul called, advising me he had spoken to Scott. The outcome of the proffer was that I would not have to testify before the Grand Jury, but Scott reserved the right to have me appear should he feel the need. My old foe, anxiety, was back.

Life went on. Every now and then, I would think about whether I would have to testify before the Grand Jury and imagined answering Scott Verseman's questions and those of his prosecuting attorneys, who I mentally pictured as "The Angry Dogs of Hell." Fortunately, I never received that dreaded call.

Several months later, I called Paul. He

advised me that Frank and Jim cut a plea deal and both of them would be going to prison. He also advised that I would not be prosecuted. That was it. There was no cheering, no high fives—just Paul's simple statement of fact. That was the last time we spoke.

I can't thank Paul enough. He was instrumental in allowing me to be there for the birth of my four grandchildren. However, here's the secret sauce that allowed this happy ending:

WINNERS ALWAYS GET UP—ALWAYS!

There is nothing novel about this statement. The American perspective is that winners always win. The truth of the matter is that they lose a lot.

On Thanksgiving night, 2015, during the half-time of Green Bay Packers' game, Brett Favre's jersey was retired. There is no question Brett Favre was one of the greatest quarterbacks to ever play the game. I looked up Brett Favre's lifetime completion statistics. He succeeded only 60% of the time. The flip side is that he failed in four out of every ten attempts. It is easy for us to focus on our failures, listen to that little voice in our head, and retreat into perpetual doubt and a life that is both safe and mediocre. Winners refuse!

Winning is a state of mind. Winners refuse to accept NO, regardless of how many times they fail. They command their inner voice to say, "I can," instead of "I can't."

My life has gone on, and I continue to get up. A few years ago, I almost died from bleeding out on the bathroom floor in the middle of the night—a complication from blood thinners. I was rushed to the hospital and spent a week in intensive care. Thanks to modern medicine, I was able to get up.

While in the hospital, I thought about how blessed I am and what is truly important in life. Looking back, I asked myself why I didn't die. I was so close. How did Lili hear my faint tapping as I lay on the floor, too week to call? After all, she is a very sound sleeper. The answer came in the form of a question. Is there something much more important for me to do with the rest of my life?

The weeks following my release from the hospital were very contemplative. I had approached life like it would never end and that I could continuously achieve higher levels of success. The Sands of Gold experience, the toll of the financial crisis, and a week in intensive care forced me to conclude that I am mortal. Along with this came the paradigm shift as to what was important to me. With the time I have left here on earth, I decided what was important to me is my family and helping others *who want to be helped*. Not everyone in a bad situation wants help. Some people take comfort in their misfortune and cannot be helped.

I did a self-evaluation. I love real estate and the challenges of finance, so why not do both? Lili and I both came from immigrant families and understand the cultural differences and legal barriers foreign-born people face when trying to buy a home and obtain financing. Know-ledgeable people stepped up and helped our families get established. We should do the same.

Lili and I have received CIPS designations (*Certified International Property Specialist*) from NAR (*National Association of Realtors*), which are awarded to those who have demonstrated proficiency in helping foreign-born clients with their real estate needs—a designation held by less than 2% of realtors worldwide. We own a brokerage company in Orland Park, Illinois, a southwest suburb of Chicago. I focus on helping my clients maximize their return on their homes and investment properties. I give back by using my team to help foreign-born clients navigate the complex processes of real estate in America.

I am also a licensed mortgage broker in Illinois and help our foreign-born clients achieve their American dreams by writing them home loans. Lili is also licensed as a real estate broker in Naples/Marco Island, Florida where foreign-born clients comprise a significant part of her business. What is unusual is that Lili's Florida clients are buying homes that most Americans would categorize as "luxury homes," and they usually pay cash.

I believe that every client deserves the best possible loan every time. The lending process allows me to look behind my clients' financial kimonos. What I see is that many people struggle with financial literacy issues. They are making bad financial decisions that long term are weakening them financially. When I meet with them, I try to provide a list of practical action items they can use to reduce debt and improve their personal wealth. This is one of the ways that I give back. The possibility of helping others is what gets me up every morning and fights the devils that wait for us all."

As the audience applauded, Max's mind was in overdrive. *Wow, what a story!* And Wayne O'Day had brought up something Max had been afraid to approach—Max, too, could have died. Why didn't he? Was there something more important that he was put here to do? How could he discover just what that was? And if he was the winner he'd always imagined himself to be, how could he get up when he couldn't even walk?

CHAPTER FOUR

M r. O'Day's speech left Max more inspired than ever to uncover what he was intended to do with his life. He knew his injuries would eventually heal, but the doctors had already prepared him that the visible injuries would go away, but the invisible ones would not. His physical abilities would be impaired. Even if he was a dreamer—and he sometimes was—he needed to accept the reality that a career playing baseball wasn't a possibility.

Which left his dad's grocery store.

Which left Max even more desperate to learn his purpose.

It weighed on his mind a great deal—he thought about it when he was doing his homework (his professors had graciously agreed to let him complete his coursework online), and he thought about it often while reading the motivational books Keith had introduced him to. It seemed that finding one's purpose and passion were underlying themes in these books—not only in success, but also in obtaining happiness. But the one thing the books didn't do was give him a fail-proof way to know just what it was that he was called to do.

The day before he was discharged from the hospital, he got the nerve to talk to Keith. Not sure how he'd take it, he went all in, telling him about the light and the voice that said it was not his time.

"Max, you're not the first person I've met who has had a similar experience. Whether it was real or not, we may never know. But I can tell you that those who have had similar experiences have felt compelled to do more and be more as a result of them. Here in the hospital, we witness many setbacks in life. It's what you do with them that counts."

"That's just it—sure, I feel disappointed that my secret dream of playing in the majors has died. Who wouldn't? But it's left me with no choice other than taking over my dad's business, which I really don't want to do."

"But you always have choices, Max. Whether

you explore them or not is up to you. It's easy to get discouraged but harder to get going."

"But what can I do?"

"If you don't mind, Max, I'd like to introduce you to a lady I know. I met Jeanne O'Neale through another physical therapist. She was disabled in a car accident, like you, and has overcome some pretty tall odds. I'd be happy to ask her to get in touch with you—with your permission, of course,"

"Really? It would be great to hear from her," Max agreed.

After exchanging email addresses, Keith declared that Max was ready for outpatient therapy and wished him well. "Stay in touch and remember, you're a fighter. Just look how far you've come."

"I don't think I can thank you enough for everything you've done for me," Max said, meaning every word.

"You can thank me by making progress. Find your dream and live it, Max. Remember, life is like physical therapy. If you take action, you'll make progress. But doing nothing will get you nowhere."

* * * *

The next morning, Max checked to see if any of his professors had emailed him. Instead, he found an email from Jeanne O'Neale, the woman Keith had talked about earlier that day. What he read intrigued him.

Dear Max,

After hearing about you and your accident, I was happy to oblige with Keith's request to contact you. Like you, I've suffered injuries from an automobile accident when my car spun out for no reason on a freeway in Santa Monica and my life came to a standstill. I found myself in a position where it was necessary to make drastic changes in my life. I've taken it upon myself to share my story in this email, with the hope that it will somehow resonate with you and help you find the answers you seek.

For starters, I became a single mother, and on January 25, 1985, the automobile accident left me totally disabled. The night before the car accident, I did a meditation that was outrageous and unbelievable. I just knew my whole life was going to change. At the time, I was a merchandise broker, and my business was about to explode. Not able to pay my bills, I borrowed money on credit cards. It got to the point where I dreaded opening my mail, letting my bills pile up and using cash advances to pay what bills I could. I felt hopeless and helpless.

A year and a half later, I pulled up my bootstraps and admitted I needed to make changes in my life. I went on a spiritual search. I listened to Napoleon Hill and started writing affirmations, including: I help lots of people, I hire lots of people, and I will have handsome men to carry me around when I get to where I can't walk. Two of those affirmations have become my reality today, Max.

Personal and professional development became part of my life. I listened to audio tapes by Carlton Sheets, Robert Allen, Anthony Robbins, Sharon Lechter, and Robert Kiyosaki. I created a new outlook when paying my bills, thinking how many people who worked at the water company would be helped from my payment. It was a whole new mindset around money. And it paid off. I bought my first rental—a four-bedroom cash cow—with no money down, even though I had bad credit. And I got cash at the closing. From there, I continued to buy investment properties.

Turning a profit, my properties were producing lots of cash flow. My brokerage business was being phased out by technology, so I was going to retire, continue buying houses, travel, and spend time with my mother. Then I went back to school—me, a single mom with four children! I started taking real estate classes, not because I wanted a real estate license, but because I wanted to learn.

That's when a friend, Catherine, approached me. At the time, she was in her 50s, didn't own a home, and didn't have any retirement plan. She needed to make a change and asked me how I did it. I told her what I'm going to tell you—that is, success depends on your attitude and what's in your head. If you believe you can achieve something, you can. I mentored her, and she soon began to read books and listen to audio tapes, too.

In our conversations, she asked me what I thought about franchises. My family actually opened an A & W franchise when I was five years old, so I knew a little about them. Anyway, when Catherine's mom had been ill three months before, I had recommended private caregivers, because I believed most agencies hired minimum wage employees who would steal her mom blind. She had the idea of opening a franchise of home care agencies where all employees would have background checks and be paid well. Because she had no money, I offered to be her silent partner. Before I knew it, things fell into place and I was a full-fledged partner, not a silent one. We were in business together. We had an office to conduct interviews, and I hired someone to run my other business so I could devote time to our new business. Soon we found an office in the perfect location and without any advertising, clients began calling, requesting our services.

Visiting Angels Eureka was born, and I actually tingled with excitement. Although the franchise had been Catherine's idea, I was invigorated, which was a good thing—it wasn't long before Catherine told me that she didn't like the business and wanted out. Max, I became the sole owner of a business I had never looked for—a business I never knew I wanted, but loved!

Visiting Angels Eureka grew, and on a Christmas Eve, I closed escrow on the building we were renting for $550,000 at a time when loans weren't going through—quite a feat for a lady who once took out cash advances to pay her bills! And I did it without spending any money of my own. Today, we have approximately 200 employees who provide quality care for the seniors in our community, and I pride myself on being a great employer. I was living two of my affirmations—helping a lot of people and hiring a lot of people.

Max, at the time, I didn't even want a business. I was retiring, but I fell into this and have been able to give something to the community that it really needed—a quality home care agency. It's so rewarding. When I hire people to help people, it's huge. It might not have ever found me, though, if it hadn't been for my experiences—if I hadn't become disabled and been buried in debt, I wouldn't have made the changes that led me to where I *am today.*

Today, I walk with a joy and freedom that most never experience. My advice to you, Max, is to close your eyes and imagine what will make you happy. How will it feel? What are you wearing? Who are you with? Live it in your mind now ... feel it with joy and emotion. Then be it for as long as you can. Make it happen. Make it yours.

If there's one thing I've learned, Max, it's that time is fleeting. We have big plans, but there is always tomorrow—plenty of time to act on them. Then we get sick or have an accident, and we've lost our chance. Don't put off your dreams. Don't put off your happiness. Embrace today and be the person you want to be, the person you can be, now.

You were given today for a reason. Your time is now, Max. It's the only time that counts. Now is the only time you can make a difference in your life and in the lives of others. Be happy now. Share joy now. I am a conscious creator. Be a conscience creator with me. We can change the world, right here, right now. It's too late to change what happened yesterday. Let go of any shame, guilt, or disappointment. Let go of those who hurt you. We are powerless now about those things. The only thing we can change is the now.

Developing my conscience contact with God and my

prayer and meditation is one of my most valuable assets. I guess you can say I saw the light—I did, by the way (I call it white light healing). I feel the energy around me and know I am one with my higher power. I know right here, right now that life is outrageous. I can achieve anything I set my mind to. So can you. You were given the gift of today—trust that it will shed light on your purpose, maybe in ways you least expect.

Please let me know if I can help you in any way—and stay in touch. I care,

Jeanne O'Neale

Visiting Angels Eureka

Max read the email twice, soaking up every word. Jeanne was a strong woman with an amazing attitude. He sent her a short email thanking her and saying how inspired he was by her story. Then he made two promises—to stay in touch and let her know how things were going … and to make her third affirmation come true and be there if she ever needed someone to carry her.

Then he followed her advice and closed his eyes, imagining what it was that would make him happy.

CHAPTER FIVE

T he next day was a busy one—Max was being discharged and receiving his home care instructions. His father was there to take him home, but when the time came, Max felt melancholy. He'd grown fond of the nurses and caregivers during his stay at the hospital. They'd been good to him, and he was surprised to realize that he was going to miss them.

His dad was being great, too. He kept talking about the fact that this was only a minor setback, and before long, he'd be back on his own two feet. In the meantime, though, he had everything ready to make him comfortable—his dad has given Max his own desk and computer in the store's office, where he could work on his online courses and also, as his dad pointed out, catch up on the changes they'd made in the store. Max almost groaned out loud when his father boasted about their new computerized inventory system.

"Besides, son," he said, "it will be good for you to get out of the house. I don't want you sitting home alone all day."

True to his word, Max went to the natural food store the next morning. Once settled at his desk, he booted up his computer, deciding to focus on his coursework before tackling the "guided tour" of the new inventory software. But he found that he couldn't concentrate on any of it. His mind was too busy reliving the past ten days. So much had transpired. So much had changed. The only good thing was he'd met a lot of great people, like Kevin and Eric—which reminded him that he'd promised to let Eric know how he was doing,

Hello,

I just wanted to let you know that I've been officially discharged from the hospital. Things are going okay—physical therapy, homework, and some work at Dad's store will keep me busy. I'm glad for the opportunity to thank you again for taking the time to talk to me. I truly enjoyed it.

Maxwell Clark

He hit "send" as his sister walked in the door.

"Hey, Max, jot down that we need to order three more cases of Calcium Carbonate, will ya? Seems the DIYers are using it make chalk paint, and we can't keep it on the shelf."

"Uh, yeah, sure," Max replied, quickly writing it down before he forgot.

Brothers and sisters, they were like night and day. His sister, Charlotte, was a couple years older than he—she'd already graduated from college and was content working at the store. More than content, actually, she was a health food guru who knew every supplement and vitamin and what they were for. And Max knew better than to get her started on organic and vegetarian foods—she could go on and on about the brands and their benefits.

Turning his attention to the tasks at hand, he completed his homework and was getting ready to send it to his professor when he noticed Eric had replied.

Dear Max,

There is no need to thank me. I enjoyed our talk, as well. If you're up to it, I'd like to invite you to one of my group's meetings tomorrow night. Nothing special—but it's a great opportunity to network with some impressive people. If you're interested, I'd be happy to have you as my guest.

Eric

It was an invitation Max found intriguing, and he quickly accepted.

The next day, Max had outpatient physical therapy. He had been given the option of using a different provider, but when he saw that he could continue therapy at the hospital on an outpatient basis, he jumped at it. After all, he knew the people there, and it might give him an opportunity to see Keith once in a while.

His body was healing, but as it did, he was required to work harder to use and develop his muscles. Each time he finished a session, he realized just how much work he still had to do, and that was before the cast on his leg was removed. Realizing that it was easy to get discouraged, he reminded himself of what Keith had said—that doing nothing would get him nowhere. So when the volunteer offered to push his wheelchair for him, he declined. "No, thank you. I have to stop by the library and return some books I borrowed. But I appreciate the offer," he said.

After taking only two wrong turns, he rolled through the library door, where a man with dark hair was placing books on the shelves.

"Excuse me, I'm returning these books— where should I put them?"

"Let's see," he replied, taking the books from Max and glancing at their titles. "You have a pretty good selection here. I'll be happy to put them back for you, maybe not where they belong, but I'll try."

"Oh, I'm sorry, I thought you worked here," Max said.

"No, no," he laughed. "But honestly, I should know where everything goes by now— I've been donating books to this library for a couple years."

"You donated these books? Wow, that's a nice thing to do."

"Well, I figured it's the least I can do—you see, everyone at this hospital took very good care of me when I was a patient here a couple years ago. Now, I want to give back. By the way, my name's Dave Rowe."

"Glad to meet you, Dave. I'm Maxwell

Clark—you can call me Max. I was a patient here, too—I was in an accident—actually I was hit by a car."

"Sorry to hear that. It's been a couple years since I was here, but it was under much different circumstances. I was rushed to the emergency room, not able to breathe, and spent a week in intensive care recovering from pneumonia. There wasn't much to do, so I managed to get in a little reading. The selection, though, left something to be desired, which is why I stop by every now and then with some new books."

"Wow, not being able to breathe must be scary," Max commented.

"It was. But now that it's over, I like to think of my stay here as a blessing. It gave me a chance to reflect on my life and make some changes."

"That sounds like me, but I'm still not sure what it is I want to do."

Dave pulled out a chair and motioned for Max to wheel himself to the table and sit with him.

"Being in this hospital gave me a chance to recalibrate my belief system and my priorities, Max. I can't say I had an out-of-body experience, but essentially my life stopped. My O2 levels had dropped to life-threatening levels, and my wife said I looked like a grey shell of a human body. I've found that when people have major setbacks, it's common for them to question their purpose. When I went back to work, I had a gut feeling of what I wanted to do professionally but had no clue as to how to get there. But I got very good advice from my mentors, and if it's okay, I'd like to share what worked for me."

"Yes, yes—please do," Max replied.

"Before my hospitalization, Max, I spent 15 years working for a global consulting firm. After my illness, with the help of my mentors, I decided I wanted to set up my own business consulting and executive coaching company, Enlightened Leadership Consulting, so I could help people who want to make a difference in the world. Today, I've broken free of the fears that a long successful career in a well-trodden field had instilled in me, and now I work with people with similar stories to help them actually live out their dreams. My priorities have changed, Max. For instance, instead of wondering if I should or should not do something, I find myself asking, 'Why not?'"

"I wish I could do that, but I'm not sure what I want to do—I don't think I ever was. I feel like I'm just living day to day, going through the motions."

"You are not alone, Max. There are mentors who can help you. They helped me. From my professional and personal experiences, I think a large portion of society doesn't truly live their life, or they simply accept their lot in life. They're not fulfilling their potential. My advice is to find a coach or a mentor who can give you objective feedback. Also, there are some really helpful tools that can give you insights into your personality and your preferences. There are some assessments that can actually help you pull back the curtain on your habits of thinking. When you're aware of your thinking habits, you can discover what has held you back and remove those barriers and internal blockages."

"An assessment test? That might really help me!"

"I'll be honest with you, there are so many tools out there it's sometimes hard to discern which are most helpful. I can definitely help you if that's something you are interested in exploring. But if you don't mind, I'd like to share another piece of wisdom I learned along the way. You're a young man, Max, with your whole life ahead of you. Earlier this year, I met a hero of mine—actually, I'd written my dissertation for my undergrad on him—and I asked him for his best piece of advice. He said, 'Start young.' Don't wait until everything falls into place to take action toward your dreams—then you'll think it's too late. When opportunities come your way—and they will—take them. We don't have time machines, so seize the moment."

"When it's all said and done, Max, we've both had wakeup calls. We were blessed to get the message that life is precious. It's what we do with that message that counts. It's not all about profits, but to me, it's about making a difference in the world. Max, do you know those people who keep saying they are going to do something different with their lives but never actually get round to doing it? Those are the people I help— I work to inspire them to take action ... immediate action. That's one reason why I donate books. It's also why I volunteer for a nonprofit organization called Good Grief, which provides free bereavement support to make sure no child grieves the loss of a parent or sibling alone. Believe me, it's been a life-changing experience that has taught me we never know what the future has in store, and just like waves of grief, we never know which wave we can walk straight through and which wave will knock us to the floor and take some time to recover from."

"That's inspiring, Dave," Max commented. "It's a great thing you're doing."

"It's the right thing to do," Dave replied. "I used to think of it as being the change I wanted to see in the world, which was my signature email, by the way. But now that has morphed into, 'Be and facilitate the change you want to see,' which ultimately means to make it easy for others to be that change, as well. I run my company, Enlightened Leadership Consulting, in that same spirit. Our tag line is, "Listen, Understand, and Inspire." My whole business is centered around listening to my clients in order to understand them and their stories and inspire them to take the necessary steps, to think bigger, or to break through their fears. Take this time to understand yourself, Max. Listen to your heart; it will inspire and lead you."

"I'm really glad I ran into you today, Dave. I

admit, I was losing hope and like you said, I'm pretty sure I was accepting my lot in life. Thanks to you, I realize it doesn't have to be that way."

"That's right, Max, it doesn't." Dave replied. "And there are always people who can help you, like the authors of these books—they're mentors, too. Reach out to people, ask questions. Let them help you. When they help you, they help themselves, too. If this is your time, Max, it's also our time, because when you take the opportunities that come your way, you can make a difference for all of us."

CHAPTER SIX

M ax was impressed. Not only had Dave experienced a life-changing event, but he used it to change his life and the lives of others. He gave his time to volunteer for worthwhile causes, donated to the hospital, and still took the time to offer advice to a total stranger.

Determined to put that advice to good use, Max began researching the assessment tools Dave had mentioned. He had no trouble finding them—a simple Google search of career assessment tools produced nearly 200 million results! The multitude of choices was so over-whelming that he decided to take Dave up on his offer to help, and in the meantime, he thought it might be helpful to learn how others had found their purpose and passion. That search also brought many interesting results, including real people who had once pondered what they wanted to do with their life and found the answers.

The third link he opened contained a video, and Max waited patiently as a man wearing a bow tie came into focus and the words "Hector Castillo, EXIT Realty" scrolled across the bottom. His face looked friendly, but most of all, there was a real sincerity in his voice, like he was speaking directly to him.

Hector first gave the viewers his background—he had been a real estate agent in New York since 1988 and then became an associate broker. He'd worked with three leading agencies in the country before stepping out and opening his own real estate company. The big move he'd made, though, was when he bought the master rights to open an EXIT Realty franchise in New York. At the time, he was married and had three children, which made the million-dollar investment a real risk.

Everything was going well—they had grown from one office to multiple offices. Then the recession kicked in, and so did reality. The entire industry felt the hit, and Hector's company struggled as the market shifted. However, he continued to do the same things they were doing—they held meetings and brainstorming sessions and continually sought ways to grow and improve. When the recession was over, Hector wanted to be ready and stronger when the next shift in the industry occurred.

They managed to survive, but the recession took a toll on his family. In the end, he and his wife decided to let go of their home, choosing instead to focus on their business, which was Hector's dream. Born in El Salvador, he'd come to the United States when he was 13 years old. He had challenges to overcome, such as learning the English language, but he didn't have to learn the desire to succeed. Breaking the low-income chain that had been in his family for generations was his motivation. It was Hector's "why," which he explained everyone must have before they can create the future they want.

"Understand and recognize what you want and why. Why do you want to be a baseball player? What triggered that in you 5, 10, or 15 years ago?"

Wow, Max thought—*he really does seem to be speaking to me.*

"Once you know your why, you can make the choices that are best for you. People don't make decisions; people make choices," he said. "But when you make that choice, give it all you have. Give it all of your passion and energy. No matter how high the wall is, find a way to go through it or over it."

"I have five kids," he continued, "and whenever they have a choice to make, I remind them that have to consider the impact their choices will have on them and others—tomorrow, next week, next month, and next year. That's why it's important to do your research before you make major choices in your life. Most people automatically run toward something shiny, but they don't take the time to know what that shiny thing really is. If you don't know what you're getting into, find an advisor—a grandparent, a neighbor, a teacher—someone who does know and can help you make wise choices."

"If you're watching this, you might be contemplating a fork in the road. Maybe an opportunity has presented itself, like it did with me, or you're just starting out. Regardless, this is your time to transform into someone better, someone greater. Keep in mind, though, that it's not only your time to pursue the dreams and life you want, but a time to recognize that it isn't all about you. Life isn't about us—it's about others. Every being came here to serve. When you make your choices and reach a level you are comfortable with—and you will—you need to go out and help others play a bigger game. By helping others succeed, you'll succeed, as well."

Hector's words left Max deep in thought. What was his "why?" He'd loved baseball ever since his dad had bought him his first glove—he loved practice and everything about it. But why?

After thinking about it, Max realized that it wasn't just baseball that he loved—he loved almost all sports. Baseball just happened to be the one where he had the most talent. He was drawn to group sports and enjoyed the camaraderie, competitiveness, sportsmanship, and teamwork that they brought into his life. The accident hadn't been just a temporary setback to Max—it had closed the door on the thing he loved the most in life. He'd been permanently sidelined.

I'm not alone, he thought. *There are thousands of people who love a sport but find they're not good enough, not fast enough, not strong enough—I'm sure they all felt the same way. And how many people had to quit playing the game they loved because of injuries? What did all of those people do when they had to let go of the sport they loved or accept the fact that they would never have the opportunity to play a sport at all?*

Had he been good enough to play in the pros? Maybe, maybe not—that was something he'd never know. But he did know baseball was a way of life for him. It was where he felt comfortable.

Then he remembered what Hector had said, "When you reach a level you are comfortable with, you need to go out and help others play a bigger game."

What had triggered Max's love for baseball in the first place was his why—and suddenly, Max knew just what he wanted to do.

CHAPTER SEVEN

A s he got ready for the meeting that night, Max found he was excited to bounce his idea off of Eric. His dad even noticed a difference in his attitude and remarked that it was nice to see him in such good spirits. "If only you had that much enthusiasm when I put you to work," he joked.

Laughing, Max only said that he was looking forward to getting out of the house for a while—he wasn't used to being idle for so long.

"You're right, son. It will do you good. If you want, I'll be glad to drop you off," he volunteered.

Max wheeled himself into the hotel lobby, where Eric was waiting for him.

"Ah, there you are! I'm glad you were able to come," he said. "I think you'll enjoy this."

"I'm glad you invited me. Actually, it gives

me an opportunity to talk to you about an idea I have."

The event room was full of people who really seemed to enjoy being there. But Eric motioned him over to a private spot where they could talk.

"So you have an idea. I can't wait to hear it."

"Well, the first time we talked, I guess you could say I was lost—I was upset about not being able to pitch this year and what that meant to my prospects in the future. And I didn't make a secret of the fact that I wasn't looking forward to going into my dad's business, either."

"No, you didn't. Has something changed?"

"I think I have, Eric. I did some thinking like you suggested and tried to figure out where I was. For a while, I was feeling like a victim of bad luck, but I started to turn that around and looked for opportunities. When I opened my eyes, I actually saw some possibilities," Max explained.

"I'm all ears."

"I realized that I love baseball, but it doesn't matter what level I'm playing. The love I've had for the game since I was a kid doesn't have to change just because I won't make the big leagues. And that made me think of all of the other people who are in my shoes—athletes who suffer injuries or kids who, for some reason, never even got an opportunity to play at all—people who love the game but circumstances have made them spectators. I want to give them the opportunity to have the fire and spirit and love that I had. I want to help kids with disabilities play sports—kids who wouldn't otherwise have the opportunity."

"That's interesting, Max, you may be onto something."

"I hope so. You see, Eric, I envision creating an environment where children can receive therapy while enabling them to participate in sports on their level with others like them. I've been through rehab and physical therapy, and I have to tell you, it's not fun. But it can be if it gives them an opportunity to do something they've only dreamed about. One thing I've realized is that the only thing worse than not being able to play baseball because of my accident would have been not to have ever had the chance to play. You see, I don't want to just help them play a bigger game—I want to share my passion and give them the chance to play that they've never had."

"Max, I think that's a great idea! Of course, your idea is new and fresh and there are a lot of logistics to work out, but I think you might be right—what an incredible way to use your experience to help others so they can have that experience, too. Max, I'm impressed with your ingenuity."

"Thanks, Eric. I needed that reassurance. I'm not exactly sure how it will work, but I'm really excited about it—maybe even more excited than I was about playing baseball! But, I don't know where to begin or what to do."

At that moment, a couple approached them.

"Hello, Garth and Hannah. It's so good to see you again," Eric said to the couple. "I'd like to introduce you to my friend, Maxwell Clark. Max, meet Garth and Hannah Watrous. Their business is unique—their company, American Hat Makers, is the number one hat manufacturer in North America."

After they exchanged greetings, Eric brought the couple up to speed, explaining Max's accident and his desire to do something different with his life. Max briefly shared his idea, as well as his concerns, mostly that he wasn't a businessman and had never run a business before.

"I'm not even sure if it can be done. Like Eric said, there a lot of logistics I haven't considered."

"Sports was a part of my life, as well, Max," Garth said. "Golf is a big part of my story. In fact, I was a scratch golfer and played golf in college. The game taught me a lot, and it made me more disciplined and focused."

"I find myself appreciating the values that sports brought into my life even more now that I cannot play," Max said. "I think that's why I feel drawn to helping others have that experience."

"Making a difference is a noble cause, Max, and I try to do it whenever I can," Hannah offered. "Just recently, I turned 40 and in lieu of birthday gifts, I raised money for a boy who has leukemia. Actually, we have quite a bit in common. Don't we, Garth?"

"We sure do. You see, Max, we also suffered a setback—we didn't have the misfortune you've had, but Hannah and I both went through recovery. We had two choices at that time—to die or take the world by storm. We chose to take the opportunities that were given to us."

"If I might ask, how did you know which opportunities to take?" Max asked.

"That's just it, Max. The excitement is in the unknown. Hannah and I actually enjoy change and the process of trying something new. I guess you can say we enjoy being uncomfortable," Garth replied. "My advice to you is to make a decision. You can always change it down the road if you need to. But when you do make that decision, chase it like it's your last day on earth."

"Most people resist change, Max. Ultimately, they don't get to reap the rewards that change can bring because they fear that they might fall short or are scared to fail. They have too many doubts and imagine everything that can go wrong. When that happens, the variables are out of control. My advice to you is to act anyway."

"Trust your intuition, Max. It's what I always do and what I always tell our children to do, as well," Hannah interjected. "Your intuition is trying to tell you something, and it rarely steers you wrong. Follow your dreams and passions, whatever they look like to you, even if it's only for one second at a time. Do what you need to do to live a life that leaves a legacy, and you won't go wrong."

"I think you're both right—I do think I'm passionate about my goal, but it's a pretty lofty one. I'm afraid that I don't know what I'm doing. Like you said, I'm afraid to fail," Max said.

"Perfectionism is a double-edge sword," Garth replied. "We want to wait until everything's perfect before making a change. You'll never get going if you're waiting for the right time. The best time to take action is now. Our business didn't start out as the number one hat company. We've built it from the bottom up. My father opened the business 40 years ago. I've worked there for 25 years and have been in partnership with him for eight years. Hannah is our director of marketing. You can't do it by yourself—it takes a team."

"How do I find my team?" Max asked.

"I can tell you what I did—I reached out to my equals and learned what they did that worked. I joined boards and became active in them. I'll soon be the incoming president of the Headwear Association Board, and I joined American Made Matters, a movement that's creating awareness of American-made goods."

"A part of those associations is giving back,

Max," Hannah said. "For instance, American Hat Makers provides headwear for the homeless. We strive to give back whenever we can, especially with our employees and staff. We promote and cater to them and mentor and love up our staff to the point where they are excited about life. They're excited about working with us and working together on our goals. When you have your own team, I encourage you to do the same with them."

"Wow. You make it sound like fun," Max observed.

"It is," Garth agreed. "It's also hard work, but this is the only life we get, Max. And even if we do have to work hard to reach our goals, it's important to remember the excitement of enjoying life. That's what Hannah and I try to do every day. Bring that excitement into your goals and life, Max, and you'll actually start to look forward to tackling something that's foreign to you. Just because you haven't done something before doesn't mean you can't do it. Just make a decision and chase it like there's no tomorrow, because if you don't, it might get too far away from you to catch it."

CHAPTER EIGHT

M ax was still contemplating the wonderful people he'd met and how willing they were to share their success with others when Eric said he wanted him to meet two of his acquaintances.

"Grant Moseley and Bryan Ells are partners in the insurance industry, Max, and I think they can give you some insight on putting your plan into action."

They crossed the room and joined the two men, who Max learned had known each other since grade school and had been on the same wrestling team together.

"A partnership is like a marriage," Bryan said. "It requires a lot of communication and flexibility, but it's been a very good experience."

The two shared some background about their insurance company, which provides insurance when other insurance companies can't. It was a unique concept and one that they thought through quite carefully. Ultimately, it was built on three concepts: other companies refer clients to them when they cannot insure a prospective customer, which turns into three givings on their end. They insure their customer and when they become eligible again, they assist in transferring them back to the original insurance agency and give a thank you to that company in the form of compensation. The last leg of their company, The We Foundation, focuses on charities. With every referral they write, they make a contribution to the foundation and let the referring agency get involved in determining the charities that will receive their donations.

Bryan and Grant had created their company with a plan, and 15 years later, they were carrying out another plan to help their business grow. Bryan explained how that came about.

"I had an encounter with an affluent businessman who was both very generous and giving in sharing his success story. He stressed the need to change your thought process in order to change your future. He asked me how much money our business generated each month, and I told him, although I was a little embarrassed. In response, he asked me a question, 'What would you consider success from the standpoint of growth?' I hadn't thought about that before, so I told him it would be nice to double our revenues, but he replied asking, 'Why not start with ten times that amount?' Then he said we needed to shift our thinking so we would know what those revenues would look like."

"There was a blueprint for what we were making," Bryan said. "We already knew the blueprint for that. We knew the resources and personnel we needed to do it. We had to think through the process for creating ten times the revenue. To create the blueprint we had to do three things: Think it, write it down, and take action."

"When Bryan met that man, it opened our mind to thinking differently," Grant shared. "We started attending seminars, and the process triggered a change that required us to think about what was possible. We also had to go through the process of removing our doubts. The subconscious mind cannot do the work necessary without a specific goal. It also can't go to work to achieve that goal if there are doubts. Affirmations and visualizations helped us with that, Max, and they can help you, too."

"Remember, the how isn't important. Don't wait for the how before creating a plan and implementing it," Bryan said. "You can always work toward it and refine your plan along the way."

"So, you're saying that I should pursue my goal, even if I'm not sure exactly how to do it yet?"

"Yes! The purpose is more important than the plan. Focus on it first and foremost. When your purpose is not clear, your thought processes can be muddied and there won't be any present-moment awareness. In order to meet your goals, you can't live in the past or in the future. It's what you do now, in the present, that will help you move forward," Grant stated.

"That's right, Max. You know what you want, and that's a huge step toward attaining it. Work toward it now and invest in the present. And if I can offer a suggestion that has helped us, attend seminars and read books like *Think and Grow Rich* by Napoleon Hill and *The Power of*

Now, a great book by Eckhart Tolle."

"As a matter of fact, I just read *Think and Grow Rich* for the first time," Max said.

"It's one of those books that gets better the more often you read it," Bryan replied. "What you'll learn from books and mentors will help you grow larger. That's true whether you're just beginning to work toward a goal or if you've been in business for many years, like us."

"But first you need that goal and you need to create a blueprint of what it looks like to you, Max," Grant added. "Align your thought processes with what's possible, and don't be afraid to think big. The bigger you think, the larger you'll grow. And the larger you grow, the larger you can give."

Max was impressed and told Eric so at the end of evening.

"Thank you for introducing me to such incredible people. I'm so inspired by Garth and Hannah's story and how they've built their business to be number one in the country. And now, they want to be number one in the world. Grant and Bryan are working toward their goal to take their company nationwide, and they so generously shared how they're doing it. All I have to do is think it, write it down, and take action," Max said excitedly.

"Max, I've found that is a common trait in successful people—they genuinely want to help others succeed. By sharing their successes, they help others realize that anything is possible. It's an education you can't get in school, but one that will help you in anything you do in life. You're fortunate—I had to go to Maui and lose everything before I was able to recognize the opportunities that I had been blind to. Some people go through the motions in life and never see the opportunities that present themselves. You're lucky to have found your purpose, Max. Don't let it go to waste."

"I won't, Eric. I guess you could say I've seen the light."

DARRYL,

DO WHAT YOU LOVE!

CHAPTER NINE

M ax took the advice he'd been given to heart. With zest, he began to visualize his idea, remembering to focus on what, not how. The more he thought about it, the more it consumed him, and before long, he found he had to struggle more than usual just to get through his homework. Reminding himself that the semester would end in just a few short weeks helped. Every day, as soon as he got done with his assignments, he turned his attention to formulating his plan.

Therapy was also a part of his routine. He did his exercises faithfully, sometimes several times a day, hoping that the extra effort would pay off and he'd be back on his feet sooner than expected. His therapists had been very encouraging, and they motivated him when he became frustrated with his limitations.

He had been in therapy for more than a month when he had the opportunity to talk to Keith again. Keith was usually assigned to the hospital patients, while Max and others received therapy by the outpatient team. However, on this day, Keith was covering for a therapist who had called off work.

"I was excited to see your name on the schedule," he said. "Let's see how much progress you've made."

After examining Max and putting him through exercises to determine his range of motion and limitations, Keith proclaimed that Max's leg was ready to move from a full cast to a brace that would allow him to flex his knee. The brace would give him the ability to move his leg without jeopardizing the pins that held the fractures in place.

"So I'll be able to walk?" Max asked, unable to keep the excitement out of his voice.

"Well, let's not jump too fast. When they remove the cast, you're going to find that your leg is weak. After all, you haven't been able to use those muscles for a long time. It will take time and more therapy before you're fully healed and able to walk independently. But, yes, you will be able to walk—but initially, only for a short time and with the aid of a walker."

Max had never dreamed he'd be excited about using a walker, but he was. Being able to stand again was a monumental step in his recovery!

"Keith, I know what it's like to lose the ability to walk and play sports—to do the things I used to take for granted. Now, I want to help others experience the things I've been privileged to know—and I want to be the one who makes it happen for them."

"How so, Max?"

"I want to open a sports therapy center for kids—where they can receive therapy and rehabilitation for their disabilities and injuries—but in an environment where they're among people their age. Eventually, I want these children and teens to be able to participate in sports that are geared for them. I want them to be able to be part of a team and participate in something that hasn't been available to them in the past. I don't know how it's going to happen, but I do know we all have disabilities—some we can see and others we cannot—and there has to be a way to give these kids the opportunity to enjoy what I've loved and taken for granted for years."

Keith thought about what Max said for a couple minutes before responding.

"If you're serious, Max, and I hope you are, I'd be very interested in hearing more about your idea. I can tell you that there is a need. I could probably fill a team roster right now with kids who would love to play baseball, basketball, or soccer—actually, any sport. It's the one door that hasn't been open to them ... but with the right therapy and some adaptations, almost every child can participate in a sport at some level."

"You think so? I just have an idea, Keith, but I have no idea how to make it happen and what it would take to make sports accessible to these kids. That's one place where I need help— a lot of help."

"Count me in, Max. I'm willing to offer my expertise and help in any way I can. I won't lie— you're going to need to provide more than a venue for sports—the kids will need therapy and training, as well. I can help you get the support you need from the medical community, too."

"That'd be awesome, Keith! You've gone above and beyond for me, and I can't thank you enough."

"Seeing you walk through that door will be the only thanks I need, Max. But for now, I'll be happy to wheel you downstairs so you can make arrangements to get that cast off and get fitted for your brace. Learning how to walk again will be difficult, but you can do it. It's time."

* * * *

Keith was right. Now that the cast was off, Max was surprised at the effort it took to move his leg. He needed a walker and a brace to get around, but he lacked strength and stamina and still had to use his wheelchair when he got tired. He was grateful that he had come this far, but he knew his recovery was going to take months, not weeks. It helped to focus on his progress, rather than letting himself become discouraged about his restrictions.

He'd been staying home more and going to the store less, using the excuse that it was easier for him to get around at home. His dad didn't argue with him—his parents had both been very supportive and willing to help him whenever they could.

That morning, his dad informed him that he was expecting a contractor at the house to set up a new home entertainment system. Joe Newkirk provided custom installations and integration of audio/visual equipment and multimedia centers. As long as Max was going to be home, he could let him in.

At 10 a.m. on the dot, the doorbell rang and Max let Joe into the living room.

"Hi, I'm Max. Dad told me to expect you—he's pretty excited about the new TV and sound system he bought."

"Hi, Max. I'm Joe. And yes, he bought a top-of-the-line system; my job is to install it so it functions well in the home. Too often, people invest a lot of money in equipment but don't realize that the installation is a crucial part of its performance."

Max watched as Joe measured the area and made what seemed complicated look easy. Curious, he asked how he learned his trade.

"I've been in this business for 23 years now, starting when I was younger than you, Max. I learned the construction trade from my dad and the electronics side of it from my mom, who worked in Silicon Valley. I first started installing electronic equipment for a large retailer—one of those big box stores. The company grew, but as it did, our commissions got smaller and smaller. So I decided to open my own business and haven't looked back. I enjoy my job and my lifestyle. It helps, too, that I have a passion for what I do. It's part of my happiness factor—I don't 'work,' Max, because I love what I do."

"That's neat, Joe. I'm in the process of planning my own business, too. Do you have any advice about getting started?"

"I'm happy to help if I can," Joe agreed. "For starters, I want to point out there will be ups and downs when you start your own business. Your success will depend on how you weather the downs—just know that you can always work through them if you're passionate about it."

"Maybe the best advice I can give is what I tell my kids, Max. That is, find what you love to do and find it fast. The world's not waiting. It won't wait. So whatever is holding you back from getting started, figure it out. Then do it, even if the money isn't there. Money isn't the most important thing. Happiness is."

Max explained his idea to Joe, then shared that he didn't have the funding to make it happen—that had, indeed, been holding him back.

"Max, my story might help you. I'm married and have four sons. When I started my business, we lived off the second mortgage on our house for two years. The third year looked more promising—we were doing better and growing. Then the market crashed. At the time, we had four kids in a two-bedroom condo and made a decision, a choice, to go into foreclosure, rather than closing the business. It was a good move, and we were able to ramp up the business rather quickly the next year. I tell you this because I want you to know that there were difficult times, very difficult times. But I loved what I did and it made me happy—that's why I never gave up."

"The recession hurt a lot of people I've talked to—that must have been rough."

"It was," Joe admitted, "but I wasn't alone—it was felt across the country and in just about every industry and trade. Some bounced back; others didn't. The key is happiness, Max. Happy people find a way to create success, but not all successful people are happy. There is a difference."

"I never thought of it that way," Max admitted.

"Most people don't—they think success will bring happiness, rather than the other way around. It's a message I try to spread whenever I speak at the high school or other events."

"I know what you mean. I am passionate about getting started. Sports was such a big part of my childhood—it was the one thing that made me happy. It didn't matter if we won or lost; I just wanted to play. So many kids are deprived of that through no fault of their own. I really want to give them that experience."

"Well, I can agree with you there. I can imagine how exciting it would be for them—kind of like their own field of dreams. Just imagine how thrilling it will be when they hear "Game On!" and for the first time, they're in the game."

"Game on ... game on. Joe, I think you might have just named the center. Game On! It's perfect!" Max exclaimed.

The two talked about the possibility for a few minutes while Joe continued working. Joe had to admit, Max's excitement was contagious, so much so that he asked how he could make a donation toward the center.

"A donation? I hadn't thought about it, but

sure, we can make that happen. If you're sure…"

"I'm positive, Max. One of the benefits of success is being able to give back. To me, it's one of the best perks there is. It's important to me to give back to the community that has been so good to me and my family and business. I donate to charities, and I sponsor events. You have a worthy cause, Max, and I'd be honored to donate to it," Joe said.

All in all, it was a great day and a productive one. His dad received the custom installation of his state-of-the-art equipment, and Max had made another friend—in the course of a day, he had named his business and received his very first donation.

Things are rolling along, Max thought as he closed the door after seeing Joe out. Stopping to admire Joe's work in the living room, he smiled as he leaned on his walker and said out loud, "Game on!"

It was time—time to share his idea with the world—time to share his idea with his family. It was time to learn the ins and outs of opening a business from someone who'd already done it and succeeded. And he knew just who to turn to—his father.

CHAPTER TEN

H e was waiting for his father that evening. He was determined that this time he would follow through and not be afraid to tell his dad the truth—that he didn't want to carry on in the family business. He'd tried before, but had always backed out. It was different this time, though, because he had another plan—one he was passionate about and could really envision.

"Hey, Dad, do you have a minute?"

"Sure, Max, supper's not ready for another half hour or so. What do you need?"

"Well, sit down, okay? I want to share something with you, and it might take a while."

"Sounds serious, son," his dad said, taking the seat next to him in the living room. "Okay, now, what's going on?"

"Well, since the accident, I've done some thinking, Dad. Some serious thinking. And I've come to realize that I really didn't have any goals in my life … I didn't have any dreams or anything that I really cared about."

"I thought you had a goal, son. You've been going to school to get your degree so you can take over the store one day."

"That's just it, Dad. It's not what I really want to do. I've known it all along—I was just too scared to tell you. I know how much it means to you to keep the business in the family, and I really did want to help you. But my heart isn't in it."

"You thought you were helping me? Son, while I always thought you'd take over the family business one day, it wasn't because I needed your help. It was because I wanted to help you. By passing down a successful business, I thought it would make your life easier. I know how difficult it can be to start from scratch."

"But what about the business, Dad? Who will run it when you decide to retire?"

"Well, Max, there are always options. I could sell the business and make a nice profit that would support our retirement nicely—or your sister, Charlotte, could take over the reins—if she wants to. Nobody knows the health food industry and the different products we carry as well as she does. So much has changed in the last decade in the industry, and Charlotte has stayed on top of it every step of the way. She might even be more passionate about the business than I was when I opened the store 26 years ago. Health and wellness isn't just her job, Max, it's her life. She lives and breathes it."

"Why didn't I think of that? Charlotte would be perfect—far better than me!"

"She's impressed me quite a bit, Max, and she has a lot of initiative—which brings us back to you. I haven't been totally blind, son. The fact that you have never been too excited about working at the store hasn't escaped me. I just thought you were young and would come around. But I'm glad that you've opened up and told me how you feel. But, I have to ask, if this isn't what you want to do, what is?"

"Well, Dad, it all started with the accident..."

Max went on to share everything, starting with the bright light and the voice that told him it wasn't his time.

"I know ... you might think I'm crazy," he said, "but it seemed so real."

"Max, I wish you had told me that earlier, when it happened. There are things in life that can't be explained—that doesn't make them less real. I do believe you, son. Whether you heard it or think you heard it doesn't matter … the fact that it left such an impression on you is what really matters."

"I know, Dad. And it made me think. A lot. At first, I struggled with it, but then I met some people who helped me realize that I have a purpose and my job is to figure out what it is."

"And have you done that, Max? Have you found your purpose?"

"I think I have, Dad. In fact, I know I have. You know I've always loved baseball and pretty much any sport, right?"

Laughing, his father responded, "I sure do. When you were a kid, we used to say that you'd rather play ball than eat or sleep."

"Well, I still feel the same way, even if I'll never be able to run or throw like I used to. But not being able to play made me realize that I'm not alone—Dad, there are so many kids who can't play, who don't have the opportunity to be involved in sports and enjoy the things I've taken for granted all of my life. I want to give them that opportunity. I want to build a sports therapy center where kids with disabilities can play sports and for the first time be part of a team. It would be a place that accommodates their disabilities or injuries and uses sports as therapy."

As Max talked, his father couldn't deny the excitement in his son's voice. "Max, you sound like me when I was a young man dreaming about opening the first natural food store in the area. And that's a good thing—when your dreams consume you, you find a way to make them happen. I can't say I know anything about sports—that's your expertise. After all, you've been an athlete since your fifth birthday when we bought you your first bat and glove. Even so, I was sincere when I said my intention has always been to help you, and even though fitness is not my expertise, I'll help in any way I can."

"That's great to hear, because there is a way you can help me. You might not know anything about fitness or sports, but it's also true that I don't know much about business—even after three years of college. I need the best teacher there is, Dad, and that's you."

"Well, son, it looks like we've got our work

cut out for us … and there's no time like the present to get started. I'll tell your mother that we'll be eating in here tonight."

CHAPTER ELEVEN

His father's business counsel was a tremendous help, and Max developed a newfound appreciation for his dad's achievements and business success. Max had a vision, and with his dad's help, he had expert advice, but he knew there was so much he didn't know. Max was intent on providing quality services, which meant finding applicable solutions for the children the center would serve. He'd been through therapy while recovering from his injuries, but he needed to broaden his knowledge about the obstacles and challenges others faced. Once again, Keith was his go-to guy, and when Max asked him for resources, he didn't fail. Not only did he offer some great information, but he suggested that Max talk to Andrew Blume, the veteran volunteer on the VA hospital's Integrative and Complementary Medicine

Committee. It was an aspect to therapy that intrigued Max, who was excited when Andrew agreed to meet with him.

When they talked, Max learned they had a lot in common. Andrew also had a vision and had been working toward manifesting a special veteran transition and training center. Although their clientele was different, Andrew's goal was similar to Max's—to assist struggling veterans toward success in their own communities, in his case, using a special wellness process. As Andrew explained, veterans' physical injuries came with a heavy emotional toll, so there needed to be a wellness process that addressed each veteran individually and holistically.

"Offering my experience and knowledge of integrative and complementary medicine, I'm assisting the VA staff as a volunteer with the Mantram (mindfulness) classes, sharing my insights and awareness as a wounded healer. My goal is to provide specialized integrative solutions and resources that address the specific needs of veterans. The two areas that are at the top of my priority list are to substantially reduce the suicide statistics, which are averaging 22 a day, and reduce the veteran homeless population."

"Wow, Andrew, I hadn't thought about that side of it—I was just focused on the physical aspects of therapy."

"It's important, Max, and there's a real need. One thing I've learned is that not all injuries are visible. Many people—children, adults, and, of course, vets—suffer from invisible injuries that can bring even the spiritually strong to their knees. From a young age, around age three, my visions and dreams guided me on an active journey of observation and experience through hardships, challenges, and achievements. I guess you could say I've had a longstanding awareness that someday, somehow, I will find solutions."

"I can relate. Like you, Andrew, my vision gets stronger, not weaker, as time goes on," Max said.

"That's your inner guidance, Max. I've found that, with the willingness to observe, listen, and follow my inner guidance through the darkness, sometimes seemingly hopeless dead ends open up into solutions for success. That's what happens when you're on a path of selfless service. While learning servant leadership, I have used my visions and experiences to give back and help others make the changes necessary to transform their lives."

"It's a good cause, and I've recently learned how rewarding it feels to help others. I have to admit if it hadn't been for my accident, I would be doing something much more selfish today," Max said.

"That's gratitude, Max. As I was guided through spiritual, emotional, mental, physical, and financial struggles, these humbling experiences taught me gratitude and inspired me to take a break from the life I faced and join the military to reassess my life plans and visions. The military presented a different and more challenging set of struggles, which eventually gave me the insight and awareness to support my fellow veterans. After serving 8½ honorable years, I confronted an unknown enemy that eluded many professionals, friends, and colleagues. Daily, I faced my own internal death and 'hell,' a process that in the spiritual community is called 'the dark night of the soul.' This darkness is common among the combat veteran population."

"Today, I'm working on different ways to face, embrace, and seek solutions for those

facing these mental/emotional/spiritual diffi-
culties, while learning the art of accepting and
embracing these difficult times as awakenings
and recalibrations."

"I'm really impressed, Andrew. Can you tell
me more about these therapies and solutions? I'd
like to know how they work and what benefits
they provide. If it's feasible, they might
complement the therapy we're already going to
offer at the center."

The two talked for an hour, during which
time Andrew explained his vision and the
healing modalities that help in overcoming the
emotional and mental issues that often present
themselves when people experience injuries or
disabilities. Andrew's passion for his mission was
very evident; Max could tell this was a topic that
was near and dear to him.

Not only did Max receive a wealth of
information, but he was so inspired by Andrew's
service and vision that he offered to help him in
any way he could. Andrew's enthusiasm was that
contagious. Max also asked Andrew if he'd be
willing to help him set up a complementary
therapy program at the center.

"Absolutely, Max. The heart of a warrior is

through selfless service. As we veterans transition from serving our country, we continue to serve by taking on new missions and tasks to serve in our communities, our country, and the world. As a matter of fact, I'm sure there are many veterans who would be happy to assist the kids—having a fulfilling purpose goes a long way toward sustainability and healing."

"That'd be awesome!" Max exclaimed. "I never thought about it before now, but it makes sense for both the kids and the vets. You've been so helpful, Andrew. I think we can do great things as we work together to make both of our visions a reality."

"We will do it, Max. I've known this was my purpose for many decades. I also knew that someday, somehow, I was going to make it happen. Like you, that time is now."

CHAPTER TWELVE

D uring the next year, Max often felt like his head was spinning. There was so much to learn, and he felt like he had to do so many things, raise money, develop a business plan, find a location, and work with advisors, investors, and architects. And these things had to be done before he could address the therapy aspect of the center. It was mind boggling and often left him feeling like he was doing many things, but none of them well. When he lost an opportunity to buy a prime piece of land, it occurred to him that maybe he was in over his head. Others had even voiced their concerns, saying maybe he should give up. Max was beginning to believe that his dream was too lofty and he'd be better off working at his father's store, after all.

Max was seriously contemplating admitting

failure when he met Scott Carson. Scott buys and invests in distressed mortgages and teaches other real estate investors how to do that, as well. He buys a lot of residential and commercial assets and works with borrowers to try to modify their mortgage and keep them in their house. It's a win-win that works for his clients and investors. When Max realized that he was going to need expert advice in financing a commercial real estate purchase, Scott was highly recommended by his banker. "Talk to him, Max. He's one of the top three in the world at what he does. If anyone can give you some insight, Scott can."

Max didn't hold out much hope when he sent Scott an email and was surprised when Scott actually replied, stating that he'd be happy to meet with him and help him if he could.

Not only did Scott give him some great mortgage and real estate investment advice, but he also offered to help him in the process. It was a generous offer, and Max knew it, but he thought it was only fair to let Scott know that he was feeling disillusioned. It was a story Scott not only understood, but had also lived.

"Max, I can relate. I also played college

ball—football. I was an ex-linebacker who had to quit playing football because my knees were shot. I think athletes struggle when they leave their sport because they miss that team camaraderie and structure. I found a way to recreate that by creating my own team over the past decade. When I became so focused on providing education and sharing my expertise, my students became my team, and it was awesome to rejoice in their victories they closed deals or raised capital. That became the highlight of my day."

"I'm glad you understand that, Scott. Frankly, I've had so many people help me, but I often feel that in the end, it's all on me. I'm used to working with a team."

"I didn't walk a road alone. Like you, Max, I literally had to hack that road and build it by myself. And it can be done. I can relate, because I tried to do too much at once, too. I was working in real estate, doing a little bit of everything to make money, like many entrepreneurs. I was making money, but I hadn't found my niche. Therefore, I didn't have a laser focus and wasn't having great success. So I had a heart-to-heart talk with myself about what I really wanted to do when I grew up. What was going to make me happiest? Now, Max, what makes someone the happiest and most successful often isn't the easiest thing to do. What I was looking at doing didn't really exist. So I stopped doing what others were doing and stopped marketing like others were and carved out my own specialty and business."

"I had faith in my ability and what I wanted to accomplish. I stopped listening to those who didn't believe in me. I was 120 percent invested—I even sold everything and left my hometown and drove across the country for three years, meeting and talking with people, banks, and clients. I was making it happen, Max. Even though people said I couldn't do it, I went and did it. And I know you can do it, too. Stop worrying about what you should be doing and what other people are saying and start doing it, anyway."

"You'll really learn a lot about what you can and can't accomplish. When you think you've seen your low and you go below that and still come out unscathed, you'll build a thick skin that will help you overcome obstacles. Sure, maybe your ego or pride will hurt a little, but you'll develop self-belief and confidence, which is really important."

"The trick is to be so focused that what others say doesn't affect you. When you put a lid on your pot, where you can't take in outside influences or negativity, you can really get the water boiling hot to create a lot of activity and energy that goes toward your goal. I stopped doing everything that took away from my ultimate goal and built an amazing business."

"But what if I fail, Scott? I'm not sure I can handle that."

"The only thing you guarantee by not trying is failure, Max. If you try and fail, you're no worse off than you were. But if you succeed, celebrate. People don't celebrate their dreams and goals. Society is always trying to make us settle so we fit inside their box. I've always found that when I was able to be myself, I've had the best results. Be yourself. Enjoy your successes and celebrate them, but learn from your failures. Learn to laugh at your failures. Who cares if you come in last? Learn from it and next time you'll come in fifth, then fourth. You didn't win every baseball game you pitched, did you?"

"Of course not," Max admitted.

"That's right, but every loss made you better because you learned from it. It's the same in business. Overnight success isn't overnight at all. For me, it's taken ten years. I don't know how long it will take you, but one success at a time, you'll get there. And when you arrive, you'll be doing something that nobody else has done."

"So you think I have a chance?"

"You sure do, but you need to stop doing it all and get laser focused on what you are doing. Being an entrepreneur isn't easy, but your dreams and goals are at stake here and worth the effort. Find mentors and other people to keep you motivated and someday you'll look back and see that you've blazed your own road. In the process, you'll evolve. Just remember to keep evolving, because that's what leaders do. You're becoming a leader, Max, and along the way, you'll find that you're winning more than losing."

CHAPTER THIRTEEN

As time went by, and Max found that Scott was right. Like most aspiring entrepreneurs, he had some failures, but they were becoming fewer and fewer. Most important, Max found that he was learning from them. When he did, he was able to make changes and get to work to create a different outcome.

Not only had Scott helped him find the perfect property for Game On!, but he'd also followed through on his promise to assist him in obtaining the right mortgage. It wasn't easy, but it was certainly worthy of celebration. There were times when he had setbacks and had to be creative, but the difference now was that he had replaced doubt with faith, which was something he'd learned from Ma Gia Tri.

Max came across Tri, as he was called, when he was listening to the radio. Max had gotten into the habit of listening to inspirational speakers and found that they really reinforced his goals and kept him focused. Tri had a weekly radio show on health, wellness, wealth, and inspirational challenges. Not only was his show interesting, but Max was fascinated with his background. A Federal Bank Examiner, Tri helped author the Banking Law and served as a key strategist on Presidential Task Forces under two presidents.

Max had received counsel from people working in many industries, and they'd all had an impact on his progress and evolution. Tri offered counsel in a different area—one that he didn't know he needed at the time, but one that he found himself turning to more and more: Faith.

Max could still remember Tri's advice. It felt like he was speaking directly to him.

"There is greatness in you. The world is dying to hear from your greatness. Let's bring it out. Let's show it."

"Each of us was created to be very unique. The world is full of billions of people, but each one of us has a different fingerprint. Your job is to identify your uniqueness and use it. We have an obligation to pass this country to the next generation and use our fingerprint to make it better."

Hearing that, Max really felt that he'd found his calling. It cemented his goals and dreams and gave him satisfaction that he was, indeed, paving the right path for not only his future, but also the future of those who would benefit from the center. It was Tri's next words, though, that really built his foundation on faith.

"Every officer of the government from the federal to the local level puts their hands on the Bible. I believe this country is built on faith. Faith does powerful things. You have to have faith as your foundation. You have to build your vision and dreams on the rock of faith, because otherwise you will build it on quicksand and will eventually fall through."

"There is nothing more treasurable than your dreams. There are a lot of dreams that are unfulfilled and talents that are not used. When you build those dreams, though, remember that the true measurement of success isn't the size of your bank account, but the size of your heart. Don't try to conquer a territory or a fortune; conquer the hearts of the people. This will be most important in this era, an exciting time for the people who have vision and faith and who think positively and constructively. They are the ones who can capture the moment and create success."

"Everyone has the right to pursue happiness. We have to create opportunities and spread the wealth for everyone. To do that, you have to have willpower, determination, and faith. You might not succeed the first time or the next, but even if you don't, you haven't failed—you just haven't received the desired result *yet.* Trust in God and have faith that you are putting your unique fingerprint on the world. Especially when your goals and dreams are to help others, know that God will lead the way."

Tri was right. Max found himself relying on faith frequently. It gave him a sense of comfort that replaced fear. It also gave him the courage to step out of his comfort zone, knowing that sometimes the outcome isn't always in our hands … and that was all right.

Max reminded himself of Tri's message and put down his checklist. The first big fundraiser for Game On! was the next day, and Max realized that he'd done everything he could do.

Rather than stressing about it, it was time to leave it to faith.

CHAPTER FOURTEEN

E xcited and nervous, Max did a quick walk through of the event room they had rented for the fundraiser to make sure everything was perfect. His mom had been in charge of the decorations, and as usual, she'd done a great job. The items for the silent auction were displayed in front of the stage. They had received donations from all over the community and even from some celebrities. But the ones that touched Max the most were from his mentors—the selfless people who had encouraged and supported him and shared their advice and experiences.

Garth and Hannah Watrous had donated a pair of their impressive leather hats, and Joe Newkirk had donated a free home entertainment system with custom installation, much like the one that he'd installed for Max's father. His mom had her eye on a quilt designed and made by Jeanne O'Neale, who had written a note wishing him the best, saying that quilting was a hobby she loved and hoped that its new owner would enjoy it as much as she enjoyed making it. Dave Rowe had sent a large package containing inspirational books and CDs from some of the biggest names—Max secretly wished he could read and listen to them all before the auction, but he knew whoever got them would put them to good use. His parents had even donated two $500 gift certificates to their store, and Charlotte had put together several large baskets filled with supplements and vitamins, along with personal health and wellness coaching sessions.

Max had connected with Hector Castillo, telling him that his video had made a difference in his life. He briefly shared the concept for Game On!, and was surprised when he received a personal reply, along with a donation toward his cause. Bryan Ells and Grant Moseley had sent a generous check from The We Foundation, along with their best wishes and an invitation to Max to feel free to contact them at any time. Other donors included Ma Gia Tri and Scott Carson, both sending wishes for great success, as well as monetary donations toward what they deemed to be a very worthy cause. And then, there was the grand prize, which made Max smile every time he saw it—a five-day vacation package to Maui, courtesy of Eric Schneider.

And those donations were just the tip of the iceberg. Their friend, Liana, and her husband had sent a gift certificate for professional landscaping services. There were gift certificates from local restaurants, celebrity autographs, sports memorabilia, and spa treatments. It had been a lot of work securing all of the donations for the silent auction, but one touched him at a very personal level. Even though he hadn't gone back to school and finished his degree, Max's baseball coach had sent him a letter of support, along with four season passes to all of the college's athletic events. At the end, he told him he was proud that he'd had the opportunity to coach him. "You were good, Max. You now have the opportunity to be even better. I believe in you."

It hadn't been easy getting to this point, and Max knew he couldn't have done it without the help of a lot of people, including his dad. True to his word, his father had advised him every step of the way—they'd crunched numbers and brainstormed ideas. When they hit a roadblock, it was his dad who encouraged him to keep going and find a way around it. And when it seemed like his dream was too far away, he reached out to his mentors for advice. They believed in him and always renewed his drive and purpose, reminding him to keep going. As Keith was known for saying, "Doing nothing will get you nowhere."

Keith had become monumental in Max's mission—he'd followed through on his promise to gain support from the medical community and had even secured donations from physicians, surgeons, OT and PT centers, and a few youth centers he was involved with. Even more, Keith was committed to the cause and had expressed interest in running the therapy segment of the center when it opened.

Max had followed through on his promise to help Andrew Blume, too. Keith and Andrew had worked together to expand the therapies they'd offer, and Andrew had agreed to serve on the advisory board for Game On! In turn, Max was sincere in his effort to help Andrew's vision become a reality. A special area of the room was designated for Andrew and a group of veterans to promote awareness toward that vision, which was coming to fruition and making progress.

Across the room, Max saw Emily, his assistant, walking around with her clipboard. Hiring a business manager had been his dad's idea. "Work your strengths, son," he'd said. "Hire your weaknesses." Emily was detail oriented, but more than that, she was driven. Fresh out of business school, what she lacked in experience she made up for in excitement. Hiring her was one of the best decisions he'd made.

Max crossed the room to talk to her. Gone were the walker, and the subsequent crutches. Sometimes, he still relied on his cane, but not tonight. There was a limp in his gait, and he'd been told that while it might improve, it would probably never completely go away. That was okay with Max; if a limp was the only long-term effect from the accident, he could live with that. Yes, there were days when he felt aches and pains, but Charlotte had recommended several products that Max was pleased to find really worked.

"Em, I'm just checking to make sure ..."

"Yes, Max, for the hundredth time,

everything is in order. And yes, your dad has already picked up Mr. O'Day at the airport. They'll be here on time."

"I don't know how you do that, Emily. You always seem to know what I'm thinking before I say it."

"Well, you've checked on Mr. O'Day's flight at least ten times today," she said, laughing.

Wayne O'Day was the featured speaker at tonight's fundraiser. Max still remembered his story and the odds he'd overcome. When they contemplated hiring a speaker, he was the first person that came to mind. He could still remember how energized he was when Mr. O'Day had said, "Winners always get up!" It was a mantra that resonated with Max and the kids he wanted to help—they were all winners in his book.

A few moments later, the caterers delivered the appetizers, and Joe Newkirk arrived to test the sound system one last time. Max anxiously stood at the door, ready to greet their guests and their guest speaker. Before long, the room was full and Max walked up to the stage to welcome his guests and introduce their speaker.

It was go time.

CHAPTER FIFTEEN

Five Years Later ...

Max and Emily took their seats in the stands next to their good friend, Liana, who immediately reached for Patrick, their one-year-old son. A lot had happened in five years—Max and Emily had worked closely together to make the center a success, and in the process, they'd grown much closer. Now husband and wife, they ran the business together. It was Emily who suggested naming their son after Max's father, who was enjoying semi-retirement and being a grandpa for the first time. It was also Emily who did the research and wrote the grant that made this second center possible, and they were there today to watch the first game at the second Game On! center.

Liana had been a big part of their life in

those five years. She and her husband had built not one, but two successful businesses together, though Liana was quick to admit that they couldn't have done it without an amazing team of employees and incredible support from their family. They'd started out with a landscaping and snow removal business, but had expanded in recent years into real estate investments. Today, their flip and renovation business was well respected in the community.

They'd first met Liana and her husband, Ross, when they contracted with them to do the landscaping for the first Game On! center, and Liana and Emily immediately hit it off and had been friends since. When Max and Emily were ready to buy their first house, they didn't have to think twice before turning to Liana. She walked them through one of their most recent flips, and they fell in love with it on the spot. Five weeks later, Liana passed the keys to their new home to them and they were first-time homeowners.

Liana was there today to support them, too—it was part of her nature. Not only did they enjoy her friendship, but she'd also been a great sounding board for them, as a family and as a business team. Max had always been impressed with their successes, but with it came some wisdom that helped remind them what was most important in their lives.

At the age of 18, Liana and her husband were living in Australia. It was her first time away from home, and in some ways, she was out of her element and comfort zone. She relied on her faith as she navigated the unknown in a foreign land and told them that one of the things that guided her was a sermon their pastor gave, entitled "Your Time is Now."

It was a sermon that reminded her to live for today and enjoy the present moment. Today, whenever she does anything, she reminds herself to live in the present, not the future. She asks herself, "What do I need to do right now?" As the owner of two businesses, it's a reminder to her that sometimes she needs to slow down and step back. She said it was far too easy to take on too much, but she learned that she has to take care of herself in order to take care of others, including their three children. Being reminded that it was her time, too, helped her through that experience and throughout her life.

"In the real estate business, Max, it's important to act quickly—if we don't, we'll miss an opportunity and someone else will buy that property. But I've also learned that sometimes it's okay to step back and take a break. If a door closes, there are always other doors. If you keep going through those doors, you'll eventually find your reward."

Helping others is ingrained in Liana's personality—it was something that Max and Emily loved about her. But she'd been a great example to them, too, especially since Patrick was born. The centers were important, but they weren't everything—they had each other and a child. It was Liana who pointed out the need to have balance in their life. "You can't work all of the time," she'd said. "You need your sacred moments, as well."

For Liana, the ultimate factor in everything she does is whether she is at peace with her decision. Everything she'd done had been a leap of faith, but it was a strong faith. Because of that, she said, she had enjoyed much success, but had very few regrets.

When they opened their first center, it was Liana who presented them with a framed picture of the Eiffel Tower that said, "Imagine Your Dream, Create Your Passion, and Live Your

Life." As Max looked at what they had created, he knew they'd done that. Their dream and passion had been fulfilled. Now, it was time for them to take some time to enjoy the life they'd created.

Liana had reminded them of that a few months before. They had been reminiscing about how lucky they were—Game On! had been a lofty dream, but it had been more successful than they'd dreamed possible. And now they were expanding and opening another Game On! in another town. They had discussed the logistics of running two different businesses in different cities and knew it wouldn't be easy, especially now that they had a child. It was Liana who made them realize that success is great, but one of its rewards is being able to enjoy it. These were the "sacred moments" she often referred to.

"There are seasons in life," she said. "We need to have seasons of success. We need to have seasons where we can reach out and help people. You've done that, Max and Emily. But in order to be truly happy, you need to have a season of rest and internal peace. I forgot that for a while and went through a difficult time because of it. Promise me you'll remember to take the opportunity to take care of yourselves and nurture each other, as well as your business."

Her words hit home—they'd already been working long hours and spending more time away from Patrick than they wanted to. So they made a choice to share their success and pass the torch of the new center onto Keith, who gladly accepted his promotion to Executive Director of the center. It was a decision they were at peace with—one they were sure they wouldn't regret. With that peace of mind, he and Emily began planning a 10-day getaway—their first vacation. They had a fantastic team who was ready to take over the reins and capable of running the centers while they were gone. It was now their time— their time to take some time off to enjoy their success and their family.

Keith walked onto the pitching mound, which, along with the bases, had been freshly painted onto the indoor gym floor. A playing field without obstacles made it possible for the kids to round the bases with their walkers and braces. It was Max's signal to come forward. His only job today was to thank the crowd and throw the first pitch.

He rose and waited for Keith to welcome the fans and introduce him. When the applause died down, Max took the mike from his friend.

"I want to welcome all of you. Game On! would have never been possible without the tremendous support and help we've received from so many people. Emily and I want to thank each and every one of you for everything you've done to make today possible." He paused for a moment, spanning the audience to find his wife and son, Liana, his parents, and Charlotte. His eyes then rested upon the children who were anxiously lined up and ready to take the field for the very first time. He thought about their parents and siblings, who were so proudly beaming in the stands. *This is what it's all about,* he thought before continuing.

"Without further ado, I want to tip my hat to our players today. They're all winners. They've worked hard, but they never gave up. The moment they've waited for is here—this is your time, teams, you may take the field."

The fans applauded as the kids took their positions. Max took the mound and threw the first pitch to the catcher, who beamed with pride as he caught it. Knowing what these kids had overcome and how hard they'd worked, Max felt his heart swell. They deserved this moment, this experience. Once again, he knew that this was what he was meant to do—sometimes, life leads us to our purpose in strange ways. Choking back a tear, he took a deep breath and felt the thrill of the moment before saying the two words the kids were waiting to hear.

"Game on!"

GREG S. REID

 Bestselling author, acclaimed speaker, master storyteller, and filmmaker, Greg S. Reid is a natural entrepreneur known for his giving spirit and a knack for translating complicated situations into simple, digestible concepts.

As an ˙action-taking phenomenon, strategy turns into fast and furious results and relationships are deep and rich in the space he orbits.

Published in over 45 books, 28 best sellers, 5 motion pictures, and featured in countless magazines, Greg shares that the most valuable lessons we learn are also the easiest ones to apply. Recently, Greg has been hand selected by The Napoleon Hill Foundation to help carry on the teaching found in the bible of personal achievement, *Think and Grow Rich*. His latest movie, *An American Hero*, features the real life story of Frank Shankwitz (founder of the Make-A-Wish Foundation), where one boy's desire inspired a man to change the world.

www.bookgreg.com
www.AnAmericanHeroMovie.com

YOUR TIME IS NOW

CONTRIBUTORS

CHAPTER TWO: Eric Schneider

 Eric Schneider is the Lead Conductor at Huron Paper Stock Co., Inc. Huron Paper Stock is a third generation family-owned and operated company that turns trash into gold in Chicago. His work-hard-to-play-hard attitude has allowed him the ability to achieve great success in business and in life. He has a passion for connecting deeply with people, finding the gold in the darkness, and living a life with purpose. Eric is the proud father to an amazing son, Levi (15), a talented daughter, Chance (12), and happily married to Christy, his anchor and best friend, since 2000. Eric completed the Curriculum for Living by Landmark Education

in 2007 and has been an active member of the Mankind Project since 2007. Both of these great experiences have provided Eric untold opportunities to exam his own behaviors and the impact they have on his family, friends, employees, and the world at large. His mission is to create a world of Cosmic, Comedic, and Soulful relationships by listening for love. He currently lives in Evanston, IL. Contact Eric at www.huronpaper.com or eric@huronpaper.com.

CHAPTER THREE: Wayne O'Day

Wayne is a Personal Finance Expert, an Illinois Mortgage Broker, Illinois Real Estate Broker, and Real Estate Investor. He helps his clients achieve their home ownership goals, improve their financial literacy, and develop a plan to improve their wealth and financial security. Clients include millennials buying their first home, foreign nationals, Gen Xers, baby boomers and, high net worth individuals. Frequently, divorce, immigration status, down payment or credit issues are keeping them from their dream. Wayne uses his expertise to find solutions that allow them to move forward with their housing and personal finance goals.

Wayne and his wife, Lili, own Premiere Plus Realty LLC, a real estate brokerage firm in Orland Park, IL. Wayne is a senior member of the Main Street Organization of Realtors Global Real Estate Committee and Lili is the current Chair. They have a home in Naples, Florida, where Lili is licensed to sell real estate. Wayne regularly consults with Lili's worldwide clients as they research and buy their dream home in the sun.

Wayne chairs a mentor group of distinguished executives whose focus is to improve the lives of those who want to Get Up but need a little help. To contact Wayne, visit his website at www.MortgageSpot.NET, LinkedIn, or call him at 708.966.6005.

CHAPTER FOUR: Jeanne O'Neale

Jeanne O'Neale is an entrepreneur, real estate investor, business coach, philanthropist, artist, parent and grandparent. Her life has always revolved around business. At age five, she moved to Eureka, where her family opened an A&W franchise. At age twelve, she began working as a Mug Washer. Before long she was teaching young adults how to make change, greet customers, and perform other duties required of their positions. At age seventeen, Jeanne became the A&W Assistant Manager. She graduated from Eureka High School as Class President in 1976.

For 25 years, Jeanne did sales and operated a merchandise brokerage business representing manufacturers and wholesalers of cosmetics, electronics, natural foods, and gifts to local retail stores. She often employed merchandisers to assist with the more than 100 product lines she represented.

Currently, she is owner and Executive Director of a large successful private duty home care agency that has served Humboldt County, California since 2006. She currently has over 200 employees providing 2,500 hours of client care each week to many local families.

She serves on many local boards and committees and has been awarded many times over for her commitment to her community. In

January 2010, Jeanne was named Business Person of the Year for 2009 by the Greater Eureka Chamber of Commerce. In September 2010, she was named Kiwanian of the Year for Eureka-Humboldt Bay Kiwanis. She now works with new business owners or those considering opening a business to give them the encouragement they need so that they also can be successful.

Her passion is fiber art. She creates art quilts using piecing, fusing, thread painting and embellishing. She is currently working on a portfolio for her first show in the summer/fall of 2017.

CHAPTER FIVE: Dave Rowe

 Dave Rowe is the CEO of Enlightened Leadership Consulting, a company that helps individuals and organizations become the best versions of their authentic selves, whether that is a person looking to make a change in their life or a company seeking to achieve its objectives (www.enlightened-leadership.co). Enlightened Leadership Consult-

ing combines more than a century of experience working in multi-national organizations with cutting-edge technologies to provide a range of mentorship, executive coaching, and learning and development consulting. Where other companies may try and sell their products and services, we partner with you to understand your needs and design a solution that inspires and succeeds!

Dave also works with Good Grief (www.good-grief.org), a charity that provides free bereavement support services to families with kids who lose a mom/dad/brother/sister to death. Good Grief's mission is to ensure that no child grieves alone, and the charity is affiliated with the National Alliance for Grieving Children.

CHAPTER SIX: Hector Castillo

Hector Castillo was a pioneer realtor in New York; he was far from wealthy; his father was a shoemaker at the time of his birth. Hector attended local schools upon arriving to the United States; his first jobs were in sales (vacuums, shoes, you name it). He worked for a local bank in New York. Later he gained interest in real estate and got his license in 1988, when he left his banking job. Hector sold over 1,000 homes and became one of the top realtors in Queens, New York. In 2002, he bought the Regional Rights for EXIT Realty Downstate NY. In only a few years, Castillo's business flourished with over 40 EXIT offices throughout NYC, LI, and now Central New York. He truly believes that challenges in life are simply opportunities that get the most and the best out of you and make you better.

In 2007 and 2013, Hector Castillo earned the prestigious award from EXIT Realty Corp International of "Region of the Year." He is a devoted family man alongside his wife, Gigi, and their five children. They enjoy sharing accomplishments, ups and downs, and support one another when they need it the most. These little moments and rituals they've created as a family have filled them with love and compassion, and they have become gladiators in suits committed to inspire the lives of everyone that cross their path.

CHAPTER SEVEN: Garth and Hannah Watrous

 Garth and Hannah Watrous are co-owners of American Hat Makers, the world's premier luxury boutique hat brand for over 40 years. Naturally they wear many hats, from the Business Owner hat to the Entrepreneurial Mindset hat. Makers, mentors, teachers and compassionate team leaders, for Garth and Hannah, Family comes First.

Hannah has her degree in Addiction Counseling and brings a compassionate and insightful mindset into every interaction she has. Dedicated to applying her heartfelt principles to her daily life, Hannah is dedicated to philanthropy and charitable giving. Last December, American Hat Makers donated over 300 beanies at the Santa Cruz Homeless Shelter. They also gift hundreds of hats each year as part of their Hat Day in the Sun event. In addition, Hannah recently raised $3,500 for a local boy fighting leukemia.

Hard working and driven, Garth learned how to be patient, disciplined, and dedicated through his lifelong passion for the game of golf. A scratch golfer, he was the 2009 Seascape Men's Club Champion and was on the San Diego State University golf team. Garth continues to refine his game in local championships. He is a board member of the Seascape Golf Course and proudly serves on the board of American Made Matters. He is deeply honored and excited to be the incoming president for The Headwear Association.

Garth and Hannah live in Freedom, California with their two daughters. They are dedicated to living each day to the fullest with integrity and honesty. Their hearts and minds are open to every possibility for growth, compassion, and connection. Leading by example and with a flair for fun and laughter, Garth and Hannah are #ComingInHot #LivingTheDream!

To connect with Garth and Hannah, call 1-800-NiceHat or send an email to them at AmericanHatMakers@gmail.com.

CHAPTER EIGHT: Bryan Ells and Grant Moseley

Bryan Ells is a native to San Diego and grew up in suburb called Mira Mesa. He met his future business associate, Grant Moseley, while a member of the high school wrestling team. Little did they know that the lessons learned on the wrestling mat would eventually hone a foundation of perseverance and determination needed to turn We Insurance into the successful business venture that it is today. Bryan has 26 years of experience in the insurance industry; 10 of those years were working directly for insurance companies like The Hartford and Geico, the other 16 years as a founding partner of We Insurance.

Bryan is an avid believer and practitioner of the power of thought and positive thinking, used to create and attract a life of abundance. Bryan lives in Encinitas, California. Email him at Bryan@we-insurance.com.

Grant Moseley grew up in San Diego, where as a freshman on the wrestling team, he met Bryan, his future business partner. He then went on to college and graduated from CSU Long Beach in 1992. Grant then lived in Northern California, Lake Tahoe, and Sacramento, before moving to Germany on a work contract in 1996/97. He then circumnavigated the globe before returning to San Diego and started an insurance agency.

Grant and his family live in Pacific Beach, CA. To contact Grant, email him at Grant@we-insurance.com.

CHAPTER NINE: Joe Newkirk

Joe Newkirk was born a go-getter. From an early age, he knew if he wanted some-thing, he would have to work for it. That's what led the self-made entrepreneur, father, husband, and business owner to become one of the preeminent custom audio/video installers in Southern California. Joe's wide-reaching circle of customers and friends seek him out not only for products but also advice. From Hollywood celebrities to CEOs and business leaders from around the country, Joe's list of clients and friends is as diverse as his business strategies. With his ever-growing business ventures, Joe preaches his positive attitude and enthusiasm for success.

Joe is a US Navy Veteran who resides in San Diego with his wife and their four sons. Contact him via email at joe.newkirk@gmail.com.

CHAPTER ELEVEN: Andrew Blume

As far back as the age of three, Andrew remembers having visions and insights that guided him on a path to educate and assist people in hardship toward interdependent sustainable solutions. Throughout myriad life challenges, spanning many facets of experience—spiritual, emotional, mental, financial and physical—Andrew recalibrated his path many times, developing the strength, flexibility, and courage to face and embrace every experience as a life lesson, knowing that eventually a solution would emerge. This process created in him an unstoppable passion and desire to serve those who struggle with no awareness or hope for a solution.

Andrew has studied and practiced in fields of wellness such as wellness consulting, spiritual counseling, bio-energetic therapies, meditation, Eyology, nutrition, yoga, Qigong, and Tai Chi. In the business arena, he has worked in management, marketing, accounting, network-ing, computer technology, and audio-visual departments, in both business and entertainment venues. His time spent in the Active and Reserve U.S. Army not only trained him to be a leader and team player, but has also given him an abiding empathy for veterans and a strong awareness of the hardships that they, and others, are facing.

Andrew is currently focused on helping expand Alectronics Research Center Intl. (1arc.org), a 501c3 nonprofit Public Benefit Program designed to educate under-served youth in grades 3-12 by bridging the gap between the arts and sciences, utilizing STEAM (Science – Technology – Engineering – Arts – Math). He is also volunteering at the VA Hospital, assisting a committee exploring integrative and complementary therapies, while he works on manifesting a special integrative wellness center to assist homeless and struggling veterans.

For updates on Andrew's work, see: andrewblume.com.

CHAPTER TWELVE: Scott Carson

 Scott Carson (aka "the Note Guy) has been an active real estate investor since 2002 and solely focused on the note industry since 2008, where he buys and sells non-performing mortgages on residential and commercial real estate directly from banks and hedge funds. His common sense approach to note investing has helped thousands of new and experienced real estate investors add notes to their portfolios.

Scott is the CEO of WeCloseNotes.com and the creator of the Note Buying for Dummies workshop that focuses on the 3 F's of Note Buying …The Find, Fund and Flip. He has purchased over half a billion dollars in distressed debt for his own portfolio and purchases assets in over 30 states across the United States.

He is a highly sought after speaker on distressed debt and was the 2014 Note Educator of the Year winner from the 28th Annual Noteworthy Convention. He has also been featured in numerous newspapers, including *Investor's Business Daily, The Wall Street Journal,* and *Inc.com.* He has also spoken at the National Association of Realtors National Convention, The National REIA Cruise, and real estate investment clubs all across the country. When he isn't traveling, teaching, or buying assets, you can find him home in Austin, Texas.

CHAPTER THIRTEEN: Ma Gia Tri

Ma Gia Tri, MBA, PMP, FISR, CGEIT, spent 28 years as Federal Bank Examiner, overseeing 325 financial institutions of the Northeast Region of United States Treasury. He was a Key Strategist Member of the Presidential Task Force to resolve the Savings and Loan Crisis and author of Banking Law (FIRREA) and regulations for the President

George Bush (senior), and a Strategist for The Presidential Task Force on Y2K Task Force under President Clinton (1999-2000). Tri is the founder of the Technology Risk Management Group for KPMG Washington DC. The CEO of Cooperation Achieves Greatness LLC, he is also a member of National Task Force to create 20 million jobs by year 2020. Tri is an inspirational speaker and wealth advisor who focuses on building wealth for America. He lectures at universities and hosts weekly radio and TV shows on health, wellness, wealth, and inspirational challenges and focuses on Baby Boomer solutions, including Medicare, long-term care, life insurance, Obamacare, 401ks, and IRA rollovers. To contact Tri, send an email to Triceospace@gmail.com.

CHAPTER FIFTEEN: Liana Clulow

Liana and her husband, Ross, live in Ontario, Canada with their three children. Their lives revolve around their work, fitting in the kids' schedules and family time whenever possible. Travelling as a family is a high priority a few times a year through road trips or flights to visit family and friends abroad. Taking time to rest and shut the phones down for a day or two helps keep things running smoothly with their businesses and kids. Design and organization are two of Liana's passions. Real estate investing is an exciting and fast-paced industry that allows her to expand her knowledge base and indulge in her creative side. The landscape business, while primarily coordinated and run by Ross, takes an incredible amount of planning and dedication on her part. Together with an incredible team, Liana and Ross truly are living the dream where they believe anything is possible! To contact her, send an email to thenan-nowflip@gmail.com.